Fixin' Up Your Van On A Budget
By Keith Sessions

TAB BOOKS
Blue Ridge Summit, PA

DEDICATION

To Sher,

My favorite person on this planet.

FIRST EDITION

EIGHTH PRINTING

Printed in the United States of America

Library of Congress Cataloging in Publication Data

Sessions, Keith.
  Fixin up your van on a budget.

  Includes index.
  1. Vans—Design and construction. I. Title.
TL298.S47   629.22′3   77-9621
ISBN 0-8306-7982-0
ISBN 0-8306-6982-5 pbk.

TAB BOOKS offers software for sale. For information and a catalog, please contact TAB Software Department, Blue Ridge Summit, PA 17294-0850.

Questions regarding the content of this book should be addressed to:

  Reader Inquiry Branch
  TAB BOOKS
  Blue Ridge Summit, PA 17294-0214

Color section photos courtesy of Travelin' Vans Magazine.

Cover photos courtesy of Leisure & Recreational Products Inc.

Preface

Not too many years ago if one were to mention the term "van conversion," few people would have understood what it meant. Today the personalized van is so incredibly popular that vans enjoy the highest resale value of any non-classic consumer vehicle on the road.

At first the only way to get a really nice converted van was to shell out an outrageous bundle and have the work done by a professional conversion shop—an arrangement hardly satisfactory for those of us waiting for our ship to come in. For the driver who carves a converted van, but *not* the monthly payments, here's a do-it-yourselfer book that fills the bill.

Professionally converted vans are being turned out in increasing numbers by an increasingly wealthy industry. If you're not ready to make a significant contribution to them, the only workable solution is do-it-yourself. With this book, and several weekends, you can do just that and manage to drive a true dream van.

Each chapter of this book covers a different phase of conversion starting with the selection of a suitable vehicle, then continuing with what will be included in the van, and how it will be laid out. The actual work begins in Chapter 3 with the installation of the floor. The following chapters cover such areas as installation of the walls, wiring, and accessories.

Converting a van yourself will save a great deal of money. But there are other advantages. The invaluable knowledge of how the van is put together that only the designer and builder can know. The experience of handling different types of tools and mastering important and valuable building techniques. And most of all, the pride of being able to say, I did it myself.

Keith Sessions

Acknowledgements

The following companies provided information for this book that not only served to make it complete but made it more applicable to the current activity in the van conversion field.

Van Conversions by Gerring, Elkhart, Indiana
Van Mail, Wheeling, Illinois
Wood Fabricators, Elkhart, Indiana
American Formed Plastics, Elkhart, Indiana
Hellstar Corporation, Wahoo, Nebraska
Jensen Laboratories, Schiller Park, Illinois
Leisure & Recreational Products,
    Lake Geneva, Wisconsin
Armstrong Carpets, Lancaster, Pennsylvania
Uher of America, Sherman Oaks, California
Stretch Forming Corporation,
    Fountain Valley, California

I'd like to give special thanks to McCrea's Van Conversions in Blue Ridge Summit, Pennsylvania, where many of the photos that appear in this book were taken.

Contents

1 Choosing The Van   7
Selection Criteria—Where to Look—When You Think You've Found It

2 Ideas and Design   30
Partitions—The Bed—The Table—Seating—Storage—The Bar—The Sound System—Lighting—Appliances—Interior Appointments

3 The Floor   53
The First Layer: Insulation—The Second Layer: Plywood—Tools—Installation

4 The Sound System   64
Cassette or Cartridge?—Stereo or Quad?—Features—Mounting—Specifications—Speakers—Power Handling—Wiring

5 Wiring   89
The Power System—Lighting—Fusing—The Hardware—Final Planning—Installation

6 The Walls   106
Preliminary Information—Specifics of Insulation—Specifics of Paneling—Specifics of Wall Covering—Specifics of Wall Material—Specifics of Tools—Installation: Insulation—Installation: Paneling—Paneling the Doors

7 The Ceiling   142
Lights—Covering Material—Installation

8 Furniture and Appliances   **160**
Furniture: Purchased—Appliances—Iceboxes and Refrigerators

9 Windows and Sunroofs   **203**
Windows—Sunroofs

10 Finishing Up   **214**
Window Coverings—Carpeting—Installation

Index   **231**

Chapter 1

Choosing The Van

While this book is primarily directed to the actual conversion process, I'd like to spend a little time at the outset to give you a few hints about purchasing your van, if you haven't bought one already. Buying a van, or any vehicle, is a big decision and should not be made in haste. When finished with the conversion process, you'll have quite a lot invested in your van—in both money and time. Making a wrong selection, getting a van that doesn't suit the needs you thought it would, is going to seriously detract from the value of your finished product. A little time spent here in deciding exactly what you want in a van could save you a tremendous amount of grief in the future.

SELECTION CRITERIA

Where you get your van is an important decision. Sometimes it isn't just a matter of going out with cash in hand and picking up a good van. It could take quite a while to find the van that's right for you. But knowing where to look will cut that time down considerably. In this chapter, we'll check into not only where to look for a good deal but what important features to look for.

Size

Perhaps it's the most important variable when selecting a van for conversion. While vans are larger than most passenger

fig. 1-1. A short van is best if only two or three people will be using it. By keeping size to a minimum, fuel is saved and cornering capability is better.

vehicles on the road, the space in them is still severely limited. It's important to choose a size that will allow you to "do your own thing" with respect to your conversion but not detract too seriously from fuel economy or handling.

Wheelbase. Size in vans is denoted by a *wheelbase figure*—the distance between the center of the rear wheel and the center of the front wheel. Vans range in wheelbase from 101 inches to 144 inches. The 101-inch-wheelbase van shown in the photo of Fig. 1-1 has 8.4 feet between the rear and front wheels. By contrast, the wheels on the 144-incher (Fig. 1-2) span a healthy 12 feet. There are many sizes between these (fortunately, because for most people the 8.4 foot van is too short and the 12 foot van is too long). The 12 foot van was designed for commercial use; but if you're planning to turn your van into a motor home, you might want to go with the larger size. Personally, I like the shorter van. Fuel economy and handling capability should improve considerably with a short van over a long one. Also, the cost of the short van is considerably less than the long one.

Generally, the longer the wheelbase, the greater the turning radius of the van. A short van may be able to execute a U-turn on a city street, whereas the long van could not. The length of the van is less important than the width or height. These two figures are of more concern to us because they more greatly affect what can be done in the interior of the van.

Width. People are often forced to tailor the interior design around van size rather than function. This is particularly true

8

of van width. Don't decide first that a crosswise bed would go great in the van and then discover later that the van isn't wide enough. If you have a special design idea that places a particular restriction on the size of your van, be sure you bear that in mind when you make your selection. There's no set formula for figuring how wide your van should be to sleep you comfortably, but as a general rule of thumb, add four inches to your height; that should give you a minimum figure. Of course, you can make special allowances for your individual sleeping habits. If you sleep curled up in a fetal ball the width of the van may not be too important a consideration. An interior width of six feet is common enough, but there aren't many used vans with wider insides. So if you're six feet tall, you'll either have to look around for quite a while before you find a van that is wide enough for you, or opt for a lengthwise sleeper.

Height. Usually the height of the van is less important to the interior design than the width. But if you are going to be doing lots of traveling and, therefore, spending lots of time in your van, you might want the ceiling to be just a couple of inches higher than usual. It can make a big difference in the "living" aspects.

Unfortunately, with the added height come some disadvantages. The biggest loss is in handling. As the height of

Fig. 1-2. If the van is to be used by more than three people or you plan on including lots of appliances, a larger van may be necessary. A van this large is commonly used commercially.

9

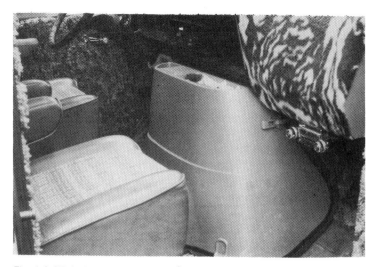

Fig. 1-3. With the engine pushed forward as it is here, the rear of the van can be accessed without negotiating a "dogbox." Also, interior noise is reduced because the engine is outside the van instead of inside.

the van increases, handling deteriorates because of a higher center of gravity. A tall van is also more susceptible to cross winds. However, the added height can be compensated for by the addition of front and rear antisway bars, overload shocks, and a front spoiler. But these modifications can run up a big bill in a hurry, so gauge how important those extra inches in height are, and you decide accordingly.

Engine Placement

If your ship came in and you're getting a late-model van, engine location is an area that you need not concern yourself with because newer vans have the engine pushed forward as shown in Fig. 1-3. Early Ford and Dodge vans were built with the engine positioned between the two front seats as pictured in Fig. 1-4. It was covered by what is called either a dogbox or engine canopy.

Let's assume you decide to get an early van with the engine between the front seats. No manufacturer builds 'em like this anymore. Ford Econolines are by far the most common representative of this type of engine placement; they were manufactured by the thousands to be used by commercial firms—electric companies, phone companies, the government—in fact, the Ford Econoline was at one time the only U.S.-made van on the road. If you want to go with an old van, your likely choice would be the Ford.

Since most old vans were used by commercial firms they are not likely to be in what you'd call "mint" condition. It may take a bit of work to make one look good. But you'll be driving what is considered the classic of vandom. There are some disadvantages however.

1. To get to the rear area of the van, you have to climb over the dogbox. The newer vans are designed so the rear of the van can be accessed by simply getting up and walking.

2. The interior noise will be greater. Since the engine is inside the van right by you, you'll have to raise your voice to be heard by a companion in the passenger seat. Your music system should be higher-powered to compensate for the extra competition.

3. You'll have to check your own oil. With the engine inside, it can only be accessed from the inside. That can be a drag when it's time to add oil or water. Instead of saying to the gas station attendant, "Dump

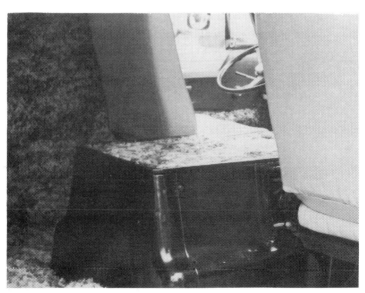

Fig. 1-4. With the engine mounted between the two front seats, several obvious disadvantages exist. The "dogbox" makes it difficult to get to the rear of the van from the front. Swivel seats cannot be installed with this type of engine placement either.

in a couple of quarts of oil if it's low, will ya?" you'll have to say, "I need a couple of quarts of oil. And do you have a spout?" You'll have to be careful not to spill any oil on your interior. If your engine overheats, and you need to add water, that can be a real problem. Lifting the engine cover and loosening the radiator cap could throw water or coolant all over your up-front interior. You can't just take the cap off and let it boil as you could if the engine were pushed forward and accessible from outside the van.

4. You can't install swivel-type seats. The position of the engine cover makes this impossible. There is not enough room between the edge of the dogbox and the door to allow a seat to swivel.

If those disadvantages sound glum, maybe you should consider the tradeoffs. There *are* some real advantages to the in-cab engine.

1. You can do things to the engine such as adjust timing and dwell with the distributor cap on. All you do is lift the dogbox, loosen the distributor timing lock bolt, drive down a quiet road or test track, and rotate the distributor as you test the van for maximum performance. Dwell angle can only be adjusted on engines with non-electronic GM-type distributors which have a small slide-up inspection and access port on the distributor cap. This is very valuable because it gives you complete control over your van's timing. Instead of just setting it to the manufacturer's specs you can find where the engine runs best.

2. You can perform minor maintenance tasks from inside the van. No longer will you have to wait for acceptable weather to change oil. You can do it from inside. In fact, you can perform a complete tuneup from inside the van.

3. The dogbox doubles as a very comfortable seat. When the van has been cruising awhile, the dogbox gets just a little warm, making it very nice to sit on. This is particularly advantageous in the winter. Instead of seating just two people up front like the new vans do, you can comfortably seat three.

As you can see, the disadvantages of having the engine inside the van may well outnumber the advantages. But those disadvantages might be something you're willing to put up with to drive a classic. Only occasionally should the position of the dogbox really inconvenience you with the biggest disadvantage being the loss of usable space. But if you can do with the slight loss of space, an early model van could save you a bundle. I personally drive a Ford Econoline because I got it cheap. Since so many were used in fleets for the electric company and the phone company, you can usually pick one up, in less than mint condition, at an auction. But more about this later.

Let's assume now that you've decided to spring with the extra cash and get a late model van with the engine pushed forward. Here are a few things to expect.

Certain vital parts like the distributor, alternator, and spark plugs are practically inaccessible to the layman. The engine cover must be removed to get to these parts on many late model vans (Fig. 1-5). This can be a big drag. Removing the engine cover not only jeopardizes your interior but it takes quite a bit of time. With the engine inside though, you just unsnap a couple of buckles, lift the lid, and there's your engine right in front of you where you can work on it, rain or no.

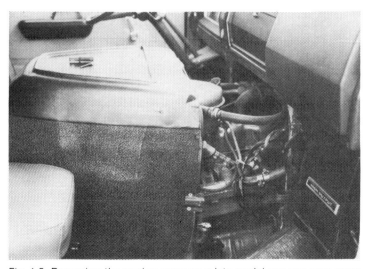

Fig. 1-5. Removing the engine cover on a late-model van can pose some difficult problems. Since it is rather large, maneuvering it into a workable position can be difficult. Also, you face the problem of getting dirt or grease on your upholstery. With the engine between the two front seats you simply lift the lid of the dogbox.

13

Fig. 1-6. Legroom is severely compromised in vans with forward-mounted engines. It's as if the vehicle manufacturers neglected the area of passenger comfort altogether.

The forward-mounted engine design will cost you lots more. Early model vans can usually be picked up for next to nothing. But you're not likely to get away with that if you've decided on a van with a forward-mounted engine; you'll have to pay probably twice as much.

Now we come to probably the biggest disadvantage to having the engine pushed forward. When I am riding around with a very special friend, I like to have her close to me. With the engine mounted between the two seats, this is no problem. But with the engine pushed forward, she has to sit all the way over on the other side of the van. It's only a matter of four or so feet, but it can seem like a great deal more. If you want your friend close while you're driving, go with the early van.

You'll notice, when you start looking at a relatively recent van, that legroom has been severely compromised because of the engine placement. In many vans from about 1972 on, the legroom is almost nonexistent. As Fig. 1-6 shows, you're forced to confine your feet to an area about a foot and a half wide. In an early model van, there is a vast difference. There is enough legroom for even the lankiest of us. Give this area special consideration if you are unusually tall or if you don't like the idea of your passenger sitting cramped.

Now to the advantages. As you'll see, they outnumber the disadvantages considerably.

The biggest advantage to having the engine pushed forward, as I've already mentioned, is the added space this type of mounting affords. Just that much added space could mean the difference between a floor that is comfortable to sleep on and one that is not.

A second advantage to having the engine mounted forward is the ease with which one can get to the rear of the van. I've developed a technique of lifting myself over my dogbox and into the rear of the van quite effectively, but your passengers probably won't be interested in learning it. With the engine mounted forward, all one has to do is walk to the rear of the van. There is nothing to climb over and nothing obstructs the path.

Swivel seats can be installed with this type of engine placement. In newer vans, swivel seats are usually available as an option. Or you can purchase them separately and install them yourself. At any rate, they can be installed with the engine mounted forward but not with the engine between the two front seats. If you really want swivel seats, the decision of engine placement is made for you. With swivel seats, the passenger up front is no longer restricted to facing the front. The seat can be turned around and the passenger can eat, play cards, or whatever. And when the van is stopped, both seats can be turned around and the driver and the passenger can enjoy the back of the van from their seats. That's nice.

The Doors

Not all doors are the same. Some are better than others. Some are downright bad.

There are two types of latching mechanisms used on van doors. The first is the lever-action type as shown in Fig. 1-7. This style of latch is no longer used on vans except those with sliding doors. Older vans, however, use this type exclusively. To close the door, it is pushed shut and a lever is moved down.

The second type of door latch—used almost universally today—is the slammable type. Instead of a lever, the handle has a button. This system is used on most cars and trucks. Unfortunately, it appears that a lever-action mechanism tends to wear out after a few years and makes it very difficult to open or close a door. My van uses the lever-action mechanism and I consider it a curse. Unfortunately, that's part of the price we pay for driving a classic. It's true that some older vans

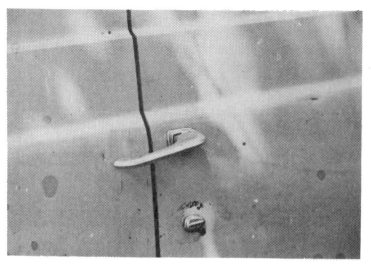

Fig. 1-7. The lever-action design of doors on early vans is cantankerous and unnecessarily complicated. Opt for the slammable type door if you have a choice.

have door latches that still work quite well, but they are exceptions. Rare is the early van that doesn't require some special coercion to get the door open or shut—a kick in just the right spot, perhaps, or an unnatural push or pull here or there. Lever-action door handles are hard to service, unreasonably complicated, and just plain cantankerous. The slammable door is so simple that if anything should ever go wrong with it, you can usually figure out the problem and fix it yourself. This type of mechanism lasts longer and reports indicate that it is virtually trouble-free for the entire life of the vehicle.

Sliding Doors

Sliding doors (Fig. 1-8) are something that have recently become available. Five years ago it wasn't even available as an option. Now you can either order it from the factory or easily find a used van with one.

This sliding door makes more sense than the conventional door. When loading groceries in a crowded parking lot, the doors can't usually be opened far enough for easy loading. But with a sliding door, there's no problem. You don't have to worry about bumping someone else's car, and there's always plenty of room to load the groceries. As an added feature, you can run with the door open—should you find it necessary.

Windows

If you are going to remodel your van with the idea of making it a family recreation vehicle, you might want lots of windows for your passengers. But if you are going another route, that of converting your van into a rolling penthouse (as I did), windows probably don't fit into your design scheme. Vans, of course, are available with or without windows, so their number and position are factors to be considered.

Most vintage vans have two windows on the passenger side and two in the rear as shown in Fig. 1-9. But they are also available with no windows on the side, if that's your bag.

Here are a few things to consider when dealing with the placement of the windows. Visibility from the driver's seat is very important. Vans are not the easiest vehicles to pilot through traffic and it is important to see where you are going. Fewer windows in your van mean poorer visibility. The major problem comes from a van with no windows in the rear doors; you'll have to depend completely on your rear-view mirrors when backing up. If you're willing to do this, great. But it's tougher by far to do it safely.

Vans are passive "ovens" of sorts; they can build up tremendous heat if they are in the sun for a substantial length

Fig. 1-8. A sliding door is a great feature and well worth the extra money it will cost you. They are difficult to close but once a technique is developed, they pose no serious problems. With this type of arrangement the worry of banging someone's door in a parking lot is eliminated.

Fig. 1-9. Two windows on the side and two in back was a very common design on early vans. Visibility is wholly adequate but proper ventilation is sadly lacking.

of time. To at least help solve the problem, consider getting a van with a few windows that open to serve as vents. The roof collects the heat of the sun and transmits it to the inside of the van. If your van will be parked in the sun for long periods, a few windows that open are particularly important to help keep the heat down.

Then there's a purely esthetic standpoint to consider. Many people opt for vans without windows simply because they think it looks better. Still others get vans *with* windows for the same reason. Long live the difference.

Ground Clearance

Ground clearance is the number of inches between the surface of the road and the lowest part of the van body. This is an important figure if you are planning on using your van as an all-terrain vehicle or as a camper. A few inches here can mean the difference between getting your van where you want it or having to park it and walk there. Six inches is a common degree of ground clearance. It may not seem like much, but that's enough to clear good-sized rock. The ground clearance of your vehicle can be increased by the addition of adjustable air shocks and by modifying the leaf-spring suspension. But consider and weigh the tradeoff carefully; the increased height will cause handling to deteriorate. Ground clearance is not a useless thing; generally, the more the better if you are planning on negotiating any rough roads. But you pay a price in handling ability. So decide according to your planned usage. If your van will be exclusively a highway vehicle, you can get by with a van that is low to the ground.

Options

When buying a used van, your choice of options is pretty limited. You're pretty much stuck with whatever came with the van when it was new. But it is still necessary for you to decide what options are necessary and useful relative to what you are going to do with your van. The list is a long one. It ranges from air conditioning to a passenger seat. You won't have to pay any extra dollars for these options directly, but they will affect the final price of your van. If you take the time to weed out useless options, you can usually save yourself a bundle.

If you've decided to get an old van, your choice of possible options is even more limited. But if you are going to get a late model van, there are a myriad of things to choose from. Power brakes and power steering are nearly universal.

When selecting possible options, be aware that they may rob your van of power. A sliding door is an option but it in no way affects vehicle performance. But power steering and air conditioning both do. They drain power in small but usually perceivable quantities that must be taken from tractive power. Here again, it's a matter of deciding what is more important to you, being cool and steering effortlessly or being uncomfortable with a slightly, but often insignificantly, more powerful vehicle.

The addition of power-drain options also affects other areas. Mileage will sometimes be adversely affected. Handling can also suffer if the options you select or want are exceptionally heavy. Your engine may have a tendency to overheat under severe ambient heat conditions with air conditioning. But most of us think it's worth the extra attention.

WHERE TO LOOK

Once you've decided on what you want in a van, there is the task of finding it. The most obvious place to look is the used car lot. This is not necessarily the *best* place to look—only the most obvious. If you're interested in getting an older van, there are several places where you might find an exceptionally good deal.

Commercial Service

Since early vans were so commonly used in industry, it stands to reason that this would be a good place to look for a van. Thousands of vans were used by the electric company for many years. What happened to those vans? They didn't just disappear. They were and are often resold to the public at auctions. It is sometimes possible to get fantastic deals at these auctions. It's just a matter of knowing when they are held and the procedure for buying there. Most of your questions about these auctions can be answered by the company itself. Just ask. They'll be able to tell you when the auctions are held and how you go about getting involved in one. The trouble is, though, that getting a van at one of these auctions usually means getting a van that has been driven as much as 150,000 miles, all of them *hard*! That's a long way for a hunk of metal to propel itself. The van you get at an auction will almost certainly need work, so be prepared. Drivers of these vans weren't concerned with keeping them looking like new. For this reason, the van you get from the electric company will very likely have a few dents in it. These disadvantages, however, are usually outweighed by the uncommonly low selling price. The companies know these vans have been mistreated and they often adjust the prices accordingly. They're more interested in ridding themselves of high-upkeep white elephants than turning a profit. If you're handy with tools, this is to your advantage, of course.

The Government

Like private industry, the government holds auctions from time to time. The most likely auction spot is a military base where you can pick up just about anything from a jeep to a half track. Vans (vehicle, light, panel, O.D.) are sold at these auctions. Like private-industry auctions, however, these vans have not always been carefully maintained. Government auctions are almost always "as-is" sales, and you can't be sure the one you want (and bid on) even has an engine unless you look first. So, unless you can see first-hand what you want, take my advice and *bid low!* This will keep the initial cost of the van low enough so you can affort to pour a little money into it. Unless you happen to like olive drab or battleship gray, the van will need to be repainted.

The Used Car Lot

As I've said, this is the most obvious place to look. When you buy a van from a used car lot, you usually have no idea as to the history of that van. It could have been driven by a gearhead. Buying a van at a used car lot may not be as safe as buying one at a government or private auction—unless the lot guarantees what it sells. This is not to say that good deals cannot be had here, though. Sometimes you can find a salesman who is willing to deal. He's hot to make a sale, regardless of the price. You can't dicker at an auction. All you can do is bid—then it's out of your hands. But when you are dealing with a salesman, it's sometimes possible to work out a pretty good deal with him.

When dealing with a used car lot, it's important to remember that it's not the same as doing business with a new car dealer. Reputation is a very important thing in the sales area and dealers usually like to maintain theirs. If they sell you a lemon, they'll usually stand behind it. But a used car lot may not. They want to make a sale. As far as they are concerned their responsibility stops there unless they specifically tell you (in writing) otherwise.

The Newspaper

So far I've mentioned only commercial places to look for a van; people who are in the business in one way or another. But the noncommercial market is larger, more competitive, and more hazardous.

The market place of the people is the local newspaper. If anyone is serious about selling something, chances are he's placed a classified ad in the paper. It is here that you can sometimes find unbelievable deals. It is also here that you can get shafted. When you're dealing with a private citizen you must be extremely careful. If you don't look out for your best interests, nobody else will. Unlike legitimate companies, private citizens are not necessarily interested in protecting their reputation. They are interested in selling. They offer no guarantees and seldom give refunds. If you buy a van from a private citizen and it turns out to be a lemon, you'll probably end up losing your investment or taking your claim to court. And courts favor sellers, not buyers. *Caveat emptor*, they say, which means "buyer beware!" If you're thinking about buying a van from some individual protect yourself along the way. Examine the van. Drive it. Get your friends to look at it. If you go to see the advertised van alone, and a problem develops after you've bought, it will be your word against the seller's. But if you have a friend along, someone who is watching all that is going on, you have someone to back you up if something should go wrong. You'll have corroborating testimony. And that can mean the difference between coming out of a sour deal with only slightly less than you went in with, and losing out all together.

There's yet another advantage to classified-ad van shopping this way. The more things you or your friends find wrong with the van, the better your bargaining position. Point out the problems to the seller. And negotiate for a better deal.

WHEN YOU THINK YOU'VE FOUND IT

Regardless of where you look, eventually you are going to find the van you want. Okay. That's half the task. You know where the van is and you want to buy it. But you must still make sure the van you want is really worth the money the seller says it is.

To make absolutely certain that you aren't getting ripped off, your best bet is to take a mechanic along and have him check the van over thoroughly. If you happen to have a mechanic friend (not just someone who says he knows something about cars), this is a good time to impose on your friendship. He'll be able to tell you if the guy selling the van is on the up and up. If there is something wrong with the van, he'll be able to tell you.

Of course, few people just happen to have a mechanic for a friend. You'll likely have to check over the van yourself. This may not be as safe as having the advice of an objective mechanic; but you can do a pretty fair job of checking the general mechanical condition of the van with only a small amount of mechanical knowledge—so long as you follow a few commonsense guidelines.

Don't even think of buying a van that you can't first test-drive. If you do you are asking for big trouble. Buying a vehicle without driving it first is like buying used loudspeakers without first hearing them. You are entitled to a test drive and don't let yourself be talked out of it.

The procedure for checking a van is relatively simple. Actually, you check the van twice. Before the test drive examine the van carefully inside and out. Familiarize yourself with it. After a test drive, the van should be checked once again. This time the mechanical parts of the van are concentrated on: transmission, engine, brakes, lighting, tires.

Before You Drive It

First, circle the van and inspect the body. Notice *any damage at all.* Call it to the attention of the seller. If the surface of the paint is broken, let him know you know it. Be critical. Every dent, every crack in the paint serves to lower the value of the van. If you find twenty places where the body is damaged, the seller will almost inevitably either hate you or drop his price.

While circling the van, inspect the tires. They should have at least a quarter of an inch of tread (Fig. 1-10); otherwise, they will need to be replaced. If the tires are in bad shape, tell the seller. In most states used vehicles must be inspected at

Fig. 1-10. If the tires on the van you want to buy look any worse than these, they'll soon need replacing. This tire may look like it is in good shape but actually it has only about 3,000 more miles of life left.

the time of sale. And insufficient tread is grounds for failing state tests. Here's a tip that might help. If your state does require vehicle inspections at the time of title transfer or sale, try to get the seller to guarantee that the van will pass the state test. You can do this in any of several ways, but the one that seems to sound the most reasonable as far as the seller's interests are concerned is this: Get him to agree to deduct all required repair costs from the purchase price. If he's been telling you about the terrific mechanical condition of the van, it will be hard for him to rationalize turning down such a reasonable stipulation.

If he doesn't buy that suggestion, here's an alternative plan he just might go for: Have *him* get the state certificate of inspection as a basic condition of sale. If he won't guarantee his van will pass inspection, and he won't deduct required repair costs from the selling price, and he won't volunteer to get the vehicle certified before the fact, you should either forget about owning this van or start dickering for a *considerably* better price.

Every little thing you find wrong lowers the value of the van. That's an important thing to remember. The doors should close tightly. There should be no gap or play after the door is closed. If there is, the door will most likely leak air around the door jamb, and that can be a very irritating thing. It will make the van drafty as well as cut down on the efficiency of the heater.

Take some time out from your body inspection to check the underside of the van. If it is a newer van, the undercoating should still be in good shape. If it has deteriorated, the van was probably driven in a wet or salty area; that *could* mean rust problems. Keep an eye out for this.

Check the transmission for leaks. Also check the oil pan, brake lines, and any other hoses for signs of leakage (Fig. 1-11). If the oil pan is wet, it probably leaks oil. This isn't a particularly expensive problem to fix, so don't let it turn you off to the van completely. But keep it in mind when it is time to come to terms on a final price. It can give you added leverage to get a better deal. If a brake line looks wet or oily, the brake system may need to be bled. This is a troublesome method of getting any air in the brake lines out. It's not expensive but it could indicate other, more expensive problems—like a bad wheel cylinder.

Fig. 1-11. Check the area around the oil pan for signs of moisture or leaks. If you find either, bear that in mind when the time comes to dicker. It may help you persuade the salesman to drop his price.

While you've got your head under the van, examine the exhaust system carefully. Check for dents, rust, and holes. If the exhaust system is dented much, the van may have seen some rough driving. If the opportunity presents itself, give the exhaust system a shake. Listen for rattles and loose joints. A loose joint means a probable leak that will have to be fixed.

Once you've convinced yourself that there is nothing seriously wrong with the outside of the vehicle, check the oil.

The Test Drive

The test drive may well be the most important check you can perform on a vehicle you are considering buying. It can tell you more about that vehicle than any other single test. So don't let it slip by. Make maximum use of the test drive. Don't be afraid to pretend the van is already yours.

Test it. Don't just drive it. Find out what it is capable of. Try to pick out any of its idiosyncracies.

Start the van. Even a simple step like this can tell you a lot about the condition of the van's engine. Notice how easily it starts. If you have to crank the starter a while before it finally fires up, there's something wrong that will need to be fixed. It could be just in need of a simple tuneup, but it could just as easily be something more serious. You really have no way of knowing without some additional checks, but it's a clue you must remember during your overall evaluation. It's best to just note the problem and use it as leverage when it comes time to deal. If the starting problem is really a bad one, though, you should have the van checked by someone who knows what he is doing.

Pay attention to the way the van changes gears. If it has a standard transmission, notice how easily the clutch is to use. Does it slip or grab? It should do neither. It should be positive but at the same time smooth. If the van has an automatic transmission, listen carefully as it shifts from gear to gear. If the engine races between gears, this is a surefire indicator of transmission trouble. It could just be that the transmission is low on fluid, so make a note to check it when you stop. But if it is full, there is something else wrong. If the van jerks when it shifts, other problems are indicated. And transmission repairs can be *very* expensive.

As you are driving down the road, try to learn as much about the van as possible. The more familiar you are with it the better equipped you are to deal later. It's important to notice little things as well as big things like transmission trouble. A window that is hard to roll up or a switch that is broken can mean a lot when it comes time to arrive at a final price. Remember, prices of used vehicles are seldom rigidly fixed. There is usually room for dealing. Unless you're buying from a private party, what you pay for the vehicle is substantially more than what the seller pays. So the seller may be willing to take a cut in profit if it means a sale. Use this to your advantage. Let him think the van is worth less to you because the cigarette lighter doesn't work.

As you are driving don't watch the road exclusively. Look around you. Move the seat to make sure it works properly. Try the horn. Search for a problem. Any problem. Everything you find wrong with the van is a step in the right direction.

Before you finish your test drive, if the opportunity presents itself, find a place where you can perform a few tests. A nice long, lonely stretch of road would be perfect. This is an ideal place to test the brakes, steering, and acceleration of the van.

Make a few quick stops from around sixty miles an hour to find out how the brakes respond. Ideally, the van should come to a stop quickly with no pull to the right or left. If it does, the brakes are in good shape. That's important because brake work can really run into money. And they are very temperamental.

Don't assume the van is in good shape if it passes the driving test. The engine could be on its last legs and there is no way you would know it. That's where we'll direct our attention next.

After You Drive It

The first thing to check after you've driven the van is the tailpipe. It's a fair indicator of an engine's condition. The inside should be a light color—tan or off white (Fig. 1-12). If it is black or oily, watch out—it may indicate serious engine trouble. The engine is probably burning oil. That means maybe rings are needed. Or some other major problem like seals. The seals themselves are not that expensive; but getting them installed is. A black tailpipe can also be caused by overrich carburetion. If the tailpipe is oily and black my advice is simple and short: Pass this vehicle up. Unless you are paying some unbelievably low price, it just isn't worth it. The total amount of money and hassle involved in getting the problem fixed may well amount to more than the van is worth.

Fig. 1-12. The tailpipe on a properly tuned and mechanically sound engine should look something like this. If the inside of the tailpipe is black or oily, watch out. Major engine trouble such as bad rings or faulty valve seals cause an oily exhaust.

Check the coolant level in the radiator. Different manufacturers prescribe different ideal levels for the coolant; but as a general rule, it should be about one inch from the top of the radiator. The coolant should be free of solid matter like specks of dirt or rust. The coolant should be a clean color. Brown or muddy coolant indicates that it hasn't been changed regularly like it should have been. Dirty coolant doesn't necessarily mean there is something wrong with the cooling system, but it does mean the van has not been cared for properly.

If the brake master cylinder is easily accessible, check it. Here again, the ideal level varies from one manufacturer to the next; but as a general rule, it should be no more than half an inch from the top of the reservoir. If it is really low, this indicates possible problems in the braking system. There may be air in the lines. If you noticed any peculiarities in the brakes when you drove the van, and the brake fluid is low, you can feel pretty sure that there is a problem somewhere.

While your head is under the engine cover, note the general condition of the engine. Is it clean and dry? It should be. If there is *dry* dirt and grease caked on the engine, there is no problem. But if the dirt is there and wet, something is leaking. Finding the leak could be quite difficult. The most you could hope for in a visual check is knowing the general vicinity of the leak. But the important thing is that the engine is wet. That fact alone should be enough to make you skeptical as to the condition of that engine. Press the seller to find out exactly what the problem is.

Once again check the oil. If it is lower than the first time you checked it, you know for sure that there is a problem somewhere. The oil should be *free* of any solid matter. To check, take a drop of oil and rub it between your fingers. Do you feel any grit? If you do, the oil is in bad shape. In fact, it could have damaged the engine. Watch out! Also check the oil for water bubbles. If you find any, disqualify this van. Something is seriously amiss. The color of the oil is another indicator of the general condition of the engine. Very black oil means the engine hasn't had an oil change for quite some time. But oil that is thick, to the point of sludge, indicates that not only has the oil not been changed for quite sometime, but the engine has been neglected.

The next thing to check is the lighting system. If you want to further assure yourself that you aren't getting ripped off, have the seller help you check the lighting system. The turn signals, headlights, hazard lights, and backup lights should be checked. Remember: Buying from a used car lot or a private individual is not the same as buying a new car from a dealer. With a new car you can rest assured that if anything goes wrong with it, the dealer will make it right. You can't assume that with anyone else. Protect yourself.

Finalizing The Deal

If, after performing all the checks I've mentioned, you're still convinced that the van is a buy, all you need to do is finalize the deal. You have to pay. This point is *the* step. You are giving some of your money away. All that you've done to this point has been aimed at protecting yourself from giving away money to the wrong person at the wrong time. If you're convinced that you aren't getting burned, you're almost home safe. But don't drop your shields yet. There's more to learn:

If you can resist your desires to own that van long enough, don't pay for it the same day you look at it. This might seem a very old piece of advice and it can be hard to follow when you're hot to play with your new toy; but it is a good idea to let your mind chew on the deal a while. Come back the following day and buy the van, unless there's a high risk of losing it to another buyer.

I know how it can feel to want something very badly and have people tell me that I should first "sleep on it." But if I'd slept on it more often before parting with my money, I would have saved myself half a life's worth of grief. And so can you.

Hopefully by this time you feel capable of venturing into the marketplace, selecting a van that is right for you and that you feel is in good condition, and feeling certain that you didn't get burned. Once you have the van, you've taken the major step in the direction of the now distant goal of owning a converted van that is suited to you and nobody else. You've made the initial investment. Now, onto the task of conversion. What are you going to do with your new van?

Chapter 2

Ideas and Design

The best way to go about planning the interior of your van is to decide what the van will be used for; then, select a theme. If you're into camping, your interior design will be substantially different from that of one interested only in a funroom or rolling penthouse. The appliances you'll want to include will vary, as will their location.

Once the use of the van is nailed down, it should be easy to select a theme. For a beach vehicle, you might select the ocean as a theme. If you're into the "good old days," a rustic theme such as that shown in Fig. 2-1 might be appropriate. If hopped up cars are your bag, there are lots of things you can do with the interior to reflect this hobby. The important thing, though, is to select a definite theme. Just throwing in lots of gear—tables, appliances, wine racks—with no specific theme in mind will make your van look like a hodgepodge; it will lack esthetic continuity. Also, selecting a theme makes it easier to imagine what the van will be like when it is finished. The decisions that must be made relative to the interior design will be easier because the theme will serve as your motif guideline.

The goal of my first conversion was to own a dream machine. I wanted the interior of my van to be me. When I wanted light, I wanted it within arm's reach. I wanted music at my fingertips—regardless of where I was in the van. And the comfort of my passengers was important. I was to put many hours of labor into my van interior. Achieving a goal such as

Fig. 2-1. A rustic theme like this might be something to think about if you have access to an old barn or somewhere you could get old wood. This van interior was done by Van Conversions by Gerring and represents one of the highest quality converted vans around.

this may seem to be a tough row to hoe, but as you read, we're sure the task will shrink to manageable size. Remember, careful planning as to what you want in the van, and where it is to travel, is a giant step in the right direction.

PARTITIONS

At one time, people who converted vans had only the factory interior that was there. Then somebody came up with an idea of adding a wall. The idea caught on. Now most professional conversions employ at least one wall or partition to isolate one part of the van from another. It probably began when people started building beds in the back of vans and wanted privacy. And there are spinoff advantages. It supplies a place for mounting auxiliary equipment—speakers, light switches, swivel lights, and storage compartments. The partition was pay dirt for vanterior designers. They began mounting television sets, wine racks, mirrors—just about anything worth having in a van.

One fairly common place for partitions is just behind the front seats (Fig. 2-2); another is shown in Fig. 2-3. At the front, the partition serves to isolate the rear of the van from the driver's area. The rear becomes a separate room. Riding in a van with a partition just behind the front seats is similar to the

Fig. 2-2. A partition like this is easy to build and provides a certain sophistication to the interior of a van. By separating the rear of the van from the front, a degree of privacy is attained that is possible in no other way.

Fig. 2-3. Partitions can be installed anywhere in a van but the most common arrangement is about four feet from the extreme rear of the van. The bed is frequently installed behind the partition both for privacy and esthetics.

pilot's compartment in an airplane. The "captain" is in the forward section operating the controls, but he's isolated from the crew.

Partitions at the rear are used most commonly to provide more privacy for a bed or sanitary facilities. The effect,

Fig. 2-4. With the bed installed behind the partition another room seems to exist. Now there are three areas: the driver area; the "living room," and the "bedroom."

pictured in Fig. 2-4, is that of another room beyond the rear partition. And to add even more privacy, some van owners install a door on the partition, making a solid barrier.

While the most common partition is solid, by no means is this the only possible configuration. Many people prefer a more open arrangement—particularly those who customize small vans. Including a partition that serves as a solid wall in a small van can make the interior look "tight" and cramped. For this reason, the partition is quite often left open, as shown in Fig. 2-5, where vertical braces are used. But this is not the only thing that can be done. Anything from bars to strings of hanging beads have been used; most are quite pleasing in effect. I used wood to build the partitions in my van because it is versatile and still relatively inexpensive. Also, I was interested in mounting lots of things in the partition, and wood is about the easiest material to work with in this respect.

Partitions also serve to give you more interior decor choices. With a partition, it is easy to generate a feeling or look of a Spanish style house: Make the partition a stylized arch. The partition gives you a place to create an image of the theme you've selected. If it is the ocean, use fishing nets and appropriate floats to cover the partition. Your van must unmistakably represent *your* theme.

Fig. 2-5. For those who prefer a more open design, vertical braces can be substituted for the solid panels of a "wall type" partition. Privacy is sacrificed but that may be something that is not needed in your van.

The time and effort involved in constructing a partition in your van will vary depending on how elaborate you want it to be. But, provided there are no unforeseen hitches in the construction process, five hours of solid work should be more than enough time to complete the entire task.

THE BED

The addition of a bed to your van's interior will probably absorb more room than any other single item. It could cost you about a third of the usable floor space. And if you are going to make the bed large enough for two, it could easily absorb up to half the floor space. That's a lot, considering the amount of time you will actually spend in the bed. Is it worth it to you? People quite often assume that they have to include a bed in their interior design because that's how it's done. They feel bound by convention. But there is no rule that says a bed must be included in the van, or it isn't a real conversion. I left the bed out of my interior because I drive an old van—one smaller than most. There simply was no room for a bed among all the other things I wanted to include. It also seemed like a large waste. I put a layer of one-inch thick foam under the shag carpet I used which made the floor more comfortable than most beds I've slept on. So there really isn't any absolute need for a bed if you consider a few workable alternatives. Rather than sacrifice valuable floor space, you might think about a bunk that folds down from the wall. This is another way to let you have your cake and eat it too. If you plan to sleep more than two people in your van, a bed could be essential. There probably won't be enough room on the floor for that many.

A bed positioned in the rear of the van behind a partition (Fig. 2-3) is the most common placement; but it is by no means the only one. The bed could just as easily be positioned lengthwise in the van. Of course, this makes the inclusion of a conventional partition to hide the bed difficult. But there are advantages. If you are unusually tall, you have the entire length of the floor in the rear of the van to use as a bed. If you must sleep more than three people in your van, a bed lengthwise is not wise; you'd be much better off making it fit crosswise. The effective length of the floor area will be increased considerably if you position the bed crosswise.

While a fixed bed will require lots of room in your van, it can also save you space. Under the bed is an ideal place to

Fig. 2-6. Besides providing a place to sleep, a bed mounted crosswise in the rear of the van like this creates an ideal storage area. Also, the wheel wells are effectively hidden.

make a storage area (Fig. 2-6). In fact, depending upon the size and position of the bed, there will usually be enough room underneath to store everything you haul leaving the rest free for extra payload. Miscellany stored under the bed and out of the way is held in place while the van is on the move. So, the floor space required can be partially reclaimed by converting the area below the bed into a storage area.

The foldaway cot, of course, is one way to have your bed and maximum space too. When it's needed, it is lowered into position and your van becomes a bedroom. If you require more than one bed in your van, or you want a larger bed, it can be arranged. Simply include two. The second bed could be positioned directly opposite the first on the opposing wall. When both are lowered into position, a single, large bed is formed.

One problem of foldaway beds is that they don't provide any storage space. When they are up, they become part of the wall—the bottom of the beds can be decorated to preserve their anonymity. Also, a certain amount of clearance is required to lower the bed into position. This means the area in front of the bed must be kept clear so the bed can fit. If your van interior design makes this awkward, you will have to consider previous approaches to the bed problem.

Fig. 2-7. Beds for vans are being marketed for the people who are not interested in doing it themselves. This unit, manufactured by Wood Fabricators is an exception to the rule that the store-bought units are seldom built better than Tinker Toys. Besides being light-weight and versatile, it is an attractive addition to most van interiors.

You do not necessarily have to build the bed yourself. Many beds are manufactured specifically for van applications (Fig. 2-7). Unfortunately, they have two things in common; the quality of construction may not be commensurate with the rest of your furnishings, and the cost is usually very high. Your search will involve several weeks of leisure browsing in van magazines, conversion shops, and even some furniture stores.

Whether or not you opt for a bed in your van, it's important that you provide adequate sleeping facilities for people who will use the van. This should be one of your objectives. If that objective can be realized without including a bed, I feel that's the best way to go. There's no need to include the added weight of a bed if it is not needed. But if your interior design warrants a bed, give careful consideration to placement. A poorly located bed can ruin otherwise ideal interior conversions.

THE TABLE

If you've decided to include appliances in your van (a stove or refrigerator, for example) you'll most likely want a table to go with them. While it is not really necessary, a table can make things a lot easier during a campout. A table not only provides a place where food can be served, it can be used to hold maps, playing cards, a TV, or a stereo. A table is a versatile tool you'll probably never regret having in your van. Unfortunately, like a bed, a table can take up a bit of space. For this reason, it is necessary to carefully plan for both the size and position of the table you want.

Commonly, tables are centered in the aft area, as shown in Fig. 2-8. Bench seats are quite often installed around the table against the wall (Fig. 2-9). If you are also planning to include a bed, however, you're going to run into problems. The table and bed must complement each other. The easiest way to do this is to design a bed which doubles as a table. This allows you to enjoy the benefits of both without sacrificing too much space. You'll be restricted in other ways, though. The bed and table cannot be used together. Then, too, it is sometimes difficult to include bench seats around a table incorporated into a bed.

If you aren't going to have a bed in your van, the problem of table placement is greatly simplified. Without the bed, you have a lot more freedom with the position of a table. If you want even more room, design the table to be removable. Out of

Fig. 2-8. The Wood Fabricators bed unit also includes a table (at additional cost) that is designed to fit into the floor-and be centered in the rear of the van.

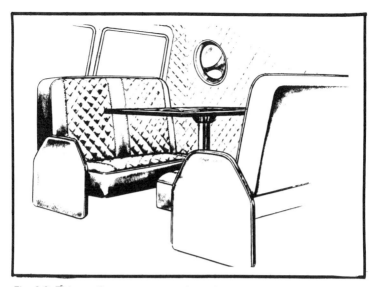

Fig. 2-9. This seating arrangement is reminiscent of many restaurants. In fact, this placement of table and couches makes riding in the van feel more like sitting in a diner.

use, it can fold against the wall, much like a foldaway bed does; or it can be completely removable, as is the unit shown in Fig. 2-10.

The underside of the table could be a mirror; even in the up position it would be functional. But when you need a table, it's there, ready to fold down to form one. Neat. The underside of the table doesn't have to be a mirror, of course. There's lots of room for creative expression here. It could be just about anything—a mural or dart board—just about anything you want.

SEATING

Depending on your purpose for remodeling a van, the importance of rear seating varies. If your van will be simply a rolling pad, rear seating won't be too important. But if you are going to use your van as a camper, or you are planning to haul people around regularly, you'll most likely want to supply them with seating.

The seats you install must hold a person comfortably, whether the van is moving or stationary. This may sound simple, but when you get involved in the actual task of seating design, you'll soon realize it's harder than you might have thought. Seats facing the rear of the van are uncomfortable for passengers when the van is moving forward. Seats positioned improperly can block rear vision for the driver. These are concerns that should occupy your mind when you are designing the seating arrangements for your van interior.

Bench seats are quite often installed around the table. This type of installation provides comfortable seating for your passengers both when the van is moving and when it is stationary. In effect, you are accomplishing two things with one installation. People can sit facing the front when the van is moving, but when it is stopped, there is more seating available facing the sides, or the rear, if that's how you choose to design your interior. A bench seat around a table is not the only way to go, but it is one of the best, in my opinion. Like the table and the bed, seats take up lots of room. But with bench seats as shown in Fig. 2-9, part of that space can be reclaimed as storage space. Also, this type of seating is one of the cheapest ways to approach the problem. In fact, if you do the work yourself, you could get by with just three 3-by-6 sheets of plywood and some upholstery material.

But if money isn't a problem, there is another way to go—factory-built seats (Fig. 2-11). You can get them to match the ones that came with the van, or you can pick up a special

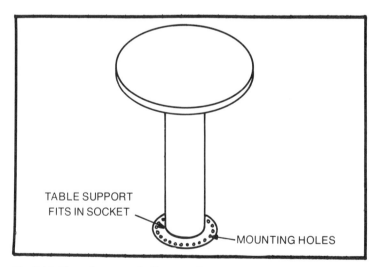

Fig. 2-10. Since the space in the rear of a van is so limited, some tables are designed to be removable when not in use. Usually a table with this feature is designed to fit into a socket installed on the floor of the van.

Fig. 2-11. For a real first-class seating arrangement install swivel bucket seats in the rear of your van. Swivel seats are much more versatile than a fixed couch or chair. This particular arrangement was done by Van Conversions by Gerring and is, by any standards, a first-rate job.

Fig. 2-12. This couch built by Wood Fabricators folds into a 72" bed when needed. The styling is not distinctive but the versatility is a strong point in its favor.

order type. Either way, it's expensive; but the finished effect is certainly pleasing! And if you don't mind paying extra, you can get seats that swivel, so the problem of them being comfortable when the van is moving is solved. Prebuilt seats can be mounted just about anywhere there is enough space. That's the primary restriction. If the seats are to swivel, they will take slightly more room than those that do not. Each seat must be positioned so there is enough clearance on all sides for it to rotate.

The most common place for swivel-type bucket seat mounting is not too far behind the front seats. However, this type of seat has been mounted far back in the van, against a wall, and even in the center of the floor. How you mount them is a matter of interior design, but plan carefully. If the seat is to go in the center of the floor, make sure it will not obstruct anything you plan to add later. For instance, you'll be disappointed if you mount a seat in the center of the floor and later decide you want to install a refrigerator and discover you can't because there isn't enough room between the wall and seat. Allow for any design changes before you position the seat. That's a way to save yourself trouble in the future.

There is a third type that could work even better than either bench or bucket. Many companies market the all-in-one units—beds that double as seats (Fig. 2-12). If you hunt around, you can usually come up with something that you can consider a good bargain. But bear in mind that the price range of these prebuilts you'll be scanning covers a limited spectrum: from expensive to downright *dear!*

Fig. 2-13. This type of seating arrangement is more suited to the "camper" conversation than the "rolling penthouse."

If you've a smidgen of mechanical ability and creativity, the most effective way to provide seating for your passengers is to build it. This gives you the most control of what your interior looks like and how well it serves its purpose. In no way are you dependent on someone else's plans. You know the unit

Fig. 2-14. The Wood Fabricators unit is designed to facilitate the installation of appliances. This arrangement is available as well as many others.

will fit because you built it! And, as it is with most of the interior, there is a certain amount of satisfaction that goes with saying, "I did it myself."

STORAGE

While the bed or seats in your van can afford some storage room, there still remains the option of including compartmental space. If a bed or couch in your van will not provide enough storage space, or if you don't want to include a bed or couch but still need the storage area, you have one option—cabinets. There are cabinets available, much like the ones used in kitchens, specifically designed for use in vans (Fig. 2-15). These cabinets vary widely in price and quality but, fortunately for the consumer, there are enough manufacturers to give you a real choice.

The most common storage cabinet is made of particle board covered with Formica. These cabinets are designed to be mounted on the wall of the van or on the floor.

The installation shown in Fig. 2-15 may appear to leave quite a bit of room for the van's inhabitants, but the fact is that cabinets take up lots of room—room you might want to use for

Fig. 2-15. If your van is to be used for camping, an installation similar to this one might be what you need. To reclaim some of the area absorbed by the appliances, cabinets are installed. Since the appliances are incorporated into the cabinets, storage area is provided with no additional loss of useable space. (Courtesy of Wood Fabricators, Inc.)

something else. The inclusion of storage cabinets in your van should be considered carefully. If there is any way that you can get by without them, I recommend that you do. Cupboards and cabinets are expensive if you buy them. And they are hard to build if you don't. Of course you could include just a cabinet barely big enough to hold the essentials, but if you "design in" lots of storage space, the living quarters in your van will be compromised. Think of an alternative if you can. Give some consideration to adding a luggage rack to the top of your van. It'll create drag on the outside of the van, but that is sometimes preferable to cramped quarters inside.

Building a bed or couch is one thing; building cabinets is quite another. The process is much more elaborate and difficult. And the finished product seldom looks as good as what you could buy. So unless you are someone who really knows his way around the wood shop, steer clear of the idea of building your own cabinets. You'd be much better off if you broke down and parted with the cash to buy them.

THE BAR

If you are going to be using your van as a family recreation vehicle you might not want to include a bar. The space that would be taken up by the bar could probably be put to better use with something that would better serve the general need of the users of the van. But if your van is to be a rolling penthouse, the inclusion of a bar is almost mandatory.

Lots of creative genius has gone into the design of bar facilities for vans. That seems to be one thing that people are dead set on including in their rolling pad. You can benefit from all this effort put forth in design by buying a few van magazines to see what others have done. You'll be surprised at some of the far out things that people have tried. Bars with running water. Bars with built-in ice crushers. Bars with wine racks. Bars with refrigerators. You name it—it's been done. Take advantage of all this design work. Get some magazines and look for a design that pleases you. Then tailor the design as your application dictates. Get your creative juices flowing and see if you can come up with some wild ideas of your own. Remember—almost anything goes.

When adding a bar to the van, don't make the mistake of forgetting that any glass has to be held in place while the van is moving. A simple shelf for glasses will not be adequate. You'll need to secure dishes so they can't slide around when the van does. That in itself will require some brainstorming. It's not simple to figure out a way to safely transport dishes and have them simultaneously accessible. But it can be done. The designs shown here are pretty functional. With limited amount of space in your van, you can't afford anything that takes up space without serving a purpose. Even better, try for as many multipurpose options as you can. Think about including a bar, for example, that doubles as a grocery cabinet when you're on a G-rated outing.

As a general rule, the closer to the middle of the van the bar is, the more secure the bottles and glasses will be. Remember when you were a kid and riding home on the school bus? The center of the bus had a pretty smooth ride, but the back was bouncy. The same effect holds true in vans.

THE SOUND SYSTEM

If you're into music at all, and who isn't, a sound system added to your van is something that you will never regret. A van sound system will sound considerably better than a similar system in an ordinary car, provided the walls of the van are insulated. And if you are planning to do a really professional conversion, you'll want to insulate the walls. The reason the system can sound so much better in an insulated van than a car is that the acoustics are much better. In a car, the speakers are in relatively close quarters. And you've little choice when it comes to loudspeaker placement and orientation. But in a van it is possible to have six or more feet between speakers. This gives much better separation than is possible in a car.

There is a great deal more room in a van and many more mounting possibilities. So there is more room for improvement. You seldom have to settle for a less than perfect speaker mounting position, a subject we'll consider at length in a later chapter.

Stereo or Quad?

While stereo might be entirely adequate in cars, it can be sadly deficient in a van. Of course if you've never heard a quad system you won't notice the loss. But if you hear both, you probably won't settle for simple stereo. Quad can be synthesized from stereo for practically pennies.

Vans are ideally suited for quad sound systems. In a car, where the amount of interior space is sorely limited, two speakers or channels is all anyone (or most of us) could want. And why not? You're never out of direct earshot of the loudspeakers. But with the added space available in a van, the benefits of going quad or four channel (instead of just two), become increasingly noticeable. And if your van will be partitioned, a multi speaker four-channel system will be almost a necessity.

Inside a van the space is much like a box. A speaker in every corner is all that is required for quad reproduction if no barrier exists between the front and rear. If you're still not convinced, let me tell you what's involved in converting from two channels to four: two extra speakers and a 50¢ resistor. We get involved in this more thoroughly in the chapter on sound systems. Whatever mode you choose, remember—the better the equipment, the better the sound. When buying sound equipment, you generally get what you pay for. If you pour lots of money into the system and do it judiciously, you're going to end up with a great sound system. If you try to get by with just a few bucks, you'll probably be disappointed.

It would pay for you to browse through some van magazines and see what others have done with their sound systems. Like the bar, lots of design work has gone into the entertainment center. Tap that work and you can come up with some good ideas. For instance, you might want to mount the tape deck on the ceiling of your van instead of the conventional place of under the dash or in it. There are advantages to having your deck mounted on the ceiling that might fit your personal application more closely. A ceiling-mounted deck is easier to reach from the rear of the van than a dash-mounted installation.

As to the mounting of the speakers, the most common technique is to flush-mount them in the walls. I think this is the best way, but not just because they are out of the way, protected from damage, and look neat. They'll sound better, for reasons we get into later. There are lots of places available in a van for speaker placement. It just takes a little creative work to pick them out. Speakers are available that are designed to mount flush up against the ceiling. Other speakers are available that are designed to be suspended from the ceiling or surface mounted. Check out the market. See what's available. You can likely find something that fits your particular application ideally. You just have to look.

LIGHTING

With the inclusion of a bar and a sound system, you are well on the way to having that dream vehicle you want. Now to set the mood, put some design work into the lighting system in your van. The bar and the sound system help the mood, but a little control over the lighting in your van can work wonders for the overall effect of the interior.

Ingenious van owners have mounted lights almost every way imaginable—in the ceiling, in the wall, even in the floor. People have added rustic "lantern" fixtures to their walls (Fig. 2-16). Swivel lights (Fig. 2-17) are common ceiling fixtures. They've used colored lights with each color group individually controllable. They've used dimmers.

If you are building a camper or utility vehicle, you'll most likely want to include some bright lights in your van so you can see well while the van is stationary. The right kind of lights can make the interior of your van seem like the kitchen in your home. If you are more of a romanticist and go in for dim lights, that can also be arranged. A lower wattage bulb will decrease the mount of light in your wan. But if you want lots of light sometimes but not so much at other times, a dimmer is the answer to your problem. With a dimmer you can have the best of two worlds. When you need the light it's available. But when

Fig. 2-16. Additional lights can also be mounted on the wall. This arrangement is not as useful as the swivel lights but the illumination is non-directional so the lighting is nicer.

Fig. 2-17. Swivel lights installed like this can be extremely useful when on the road.

you are ready for a nice mood, listening to some music and drinking some wine, the lights can be turned down.

APPLIANCES

If camping is more your bag than romance, you'll most likely want to include a few appliances to make life easier in the wild. Your choices are great. Refrigerators, sinks, stoves, 12V electric can openers, and heaters are just some of what you have to choose from.

Adding appliances does increase the weight of your vehicle, and you'll be giving up room to accommodate them. A refrigerator or stove will add approximately 100 pounds to the weight of your vehicle and take up about a 3-foot square of space on the floor. But the advantages you'll accrue from the appliances may more than offset the added weight and loss of space. Having running water or being able to keep drinks cold is a strong incentive to make room in the van for the appliances, even if it means being a little cramped.

The location of the appliances is something that you should work out on paper. But to give you a general idea of what different mounting ideas will look like, Figs. 2-18 and 2-19 show what most people are doing with appliances these days. Cabinets are quite frequently installed in conjunction with a sink, stove, or refrigerator, and give the van a definite camper appearance. They too absorb lots of space, and between the cabinets and the appliances, there is usually not much room left over for the person who must use them. But careful planning can at least reduce this problem to a manageable level. As is apparent in Fig. 2-18, there is enough space available to mount appliances as well as cabinets. Slightly cramped? Yes—but functional.

INTERIOR APPOINTMENTS

All the things I've talked about so far primarily affect how well the van serves your wants and needs in lighting, sound systems, seating, tables, and appliances. All these things make your van what you want it to be. But esthetic design will greatly affect how your van looks when you are finished. The color of the walls and carpet, the type of fixtures for lighting, the design of all the little things that go into a van but aren't always that noticeble play a more important role than anything I've discussed so far in the "look" of the interior of your van, and they warrant your attention just as much as any of the other areas.

If you look through van magazines you will probably notice a common element in all the interior designs—they tend to be gaudy. People go nuts with fur and carpet. Tackiness seems the order of the day. Fur on the ceiling. Fur on the walls.

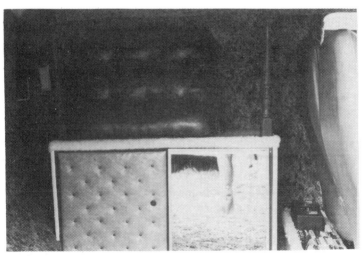

Fig. 2-18. Here a refrigerator is incorporated into a basic cabinet. The door is mirrored to add the feeling of spaciousness.

Fig. 2-19. In this installation the refrigerator and wine rack are incorporated into the same unit. Also valuable counter space is provided.

51

Hanging beer cans. The interiors sometimes look more like cathouses than pads. A neat, organized interior design is almost unheard of today. Don't let this deter you from pursuing it, though. The fact that they are not prevalent doesn't mean they aren't as good.

Of course the subject of taste in interior design is completely subjective. What I call tacky you might call beautiful. And vice versa. But if you're interested in making your van truly unique, steer clear of the stock interior designs. Try to come up with something that hasn't been used as much as fur. Upholstery material, mirrors, just about anything you'd like to try, might be an improvement over the trite banality of the overdone.

What you use to cover the walls will affect the look of the interior more than anything else. The color should be coordinated with the rest of the interior. The decisions you make here won't affect the performance of your van, only its appearance; but don't let this fact trick you into underestimating the importance of careful planning of the interior esthetics.

So much for dreaming. It's time to move on to the actual conversion process. Once you get the van and decide what you want to do with it, the real work begins.

Chapter 3

The Floor

Up to now, we have been primarily concerned with what to do with your van. This chapter begins the actual task of remodeling. We'll start at the bottom—the floor.

To do a really professional job, the first thing down should be a layer of one-inch thick fiberglass insulation. This will help isolate the interior of the van from cold and road noise. The second layer of the floor should be 1/4 or 1/2 inch plywood.

THE FIRST LAYER: INSULATION

A layer of fiberglass insulation may seem to be an unnecessary step, but if you are planning to use the van where it's cold, it should definitely be included. The floor represents an area where a significant amount of heat is lost. Insulation helps prevent this. Also, it will help to keep out road noise. If you are really concerned with saving money, the layer of insulation could be eliminated. But if you're interested in doing a first class job, include it. The type of insulation you'll need is available at virtually all hardware stores and lumber yards. You'll need about 27 feet of it in the standard width of 24 inches. One inch is an ideal thickness. It's easier and cheaper to work with than thicker types.

There are two types of fiberglass insulation commonly available. One has a paper backing; the other does not. Be sure to buy the kind with the paper backing. It's easier to use because the paper acts as a barrier between you and the fiberglass. You'll see why this is important a little later. It'll cost slightly more but it is well worth it.

THE SECOND LAYER: PLYWOOD

A layer of plywood follows the layer of insulation. This is the actual flooring material. Here again, there is room to skimp. Some people use particle board, a much cheaper alternative. But unfortunately, with the reduced cost come some disadvantages. Particle board is very heavy. One sheet 4-ft wide, 8-ft long, and a 1/2-in. thick weighs around 60 pounds of extra dead weight you'll be hauling. Particle board is also very difficult to cut. It is dense and, so, is hard on sabre saw blades. Plywood, on the other hand, is light and easy to cut. It is much stronger than particle board so you can get by with much thinner stock. Two pieces 4-ft wide, 8-ft long, and 1/4 in. thick will be ideal. If you plan to haul heavy items such as motorcycles, tools, or appliances, consider using 1/2-in. thick plywood instead of the 1/4-in. stock. It'll cost more than twice as much, but you'll have the satisfaction of knowing that your floor is strong enough to hold whatever you put on it. One sheet will weigh approximately twenty pounds and will be much easier to handle.

The salesman may try to sell you outdoor plywood. If it costs more than the indoor type, don't buy it. Outdoor plywood is specially treated to resist the elements—rain, sun, cold, etc. Since your floor won't be exposed to any of these things, there's no need to use the outdoor type.

So far your shopping list for the floor should include the following items.

- A 27-foot roll of 24-in. wide, 1-in. thick insulation.
- Two 4 × 8 sheets of 1/4- or 1/2-in. thick plywood.

TOOLS

Hands have been said to be the most versatile tools ever created, but in this case, you'll need something more. The following list encompasses all the basic tools needed to install the floor in your van. Generally, all the tools on the list are needed in this installation step. Perhaps you will be tempted to install the floor with far fewer tools than you need. This will only lead to needless frustration. Take the time to gather all tools you need to do the job right, and *then* begin the actual task.

Required van conversion tools.

- Ten foot tape measure.
- Suitable length (25 foot or more) extension cord.
- Sabre saw.
- Variable-speed electric drill with screwdriver bit.
- Felt-tip marker.
- Standard flat blade screwdriver.
- Philips screwdriver.
- Self-tapping sheet metal screws 1 in. long.
- Scissors.

When you're finally ready to begin the installation process, gather everything together—insulation, tools, everything—so you know where everything is when you need it. Then you're ready to go!

INSTALLATION

Before you begin measuring or cutting, remove the two front seats from the van completely. The floor won't extend any farther forward than the back of the seats, but the extra room will, make the job much easier. Remove any other junk from the van—spare tire, jack, beer cans. Get it all out of your way. You'll find, when you get to a point where it is necessary to maneuver the plywood into place, it'll take all the room. Anything on the floor that isn't permanently attached should be removed.

Next, scout around for any holes in the floor. Often, there are small holes from rust or someone who has drilled holes in the floor for some previous project. Every hole must be patched before the floor can be installed. Even if the hole is just a tiny one, patch it. You'd be surprised how much water can come through a small hole. And if water does find its way in, you're in trouble. The water will begin by destroying the insulation, and then it will begin working on the plywood. Ultimately, the carpet on the floor will become damaged. This may sound a bit on the exaggerated side, but the point is, if the hole is not patched now, when will it be patched? Once the floor is installed, that's it. You can't very well tear it up to fix a hole. Yet that's what will have to be done if the hole can't be repaired from the underside of the van. Invest a couple bucks in a tube of silicone sealant. It will patch the small holes beautifully (Fig. 3-1). For the larger holes, you may need some body putty. Both are available at most department, hardware, and auto supply stores.

Fitting The Plywood

Before the first layer (the insulation) is installed, the plywood should be sized and cut to fit the floor, so when the time comes to install it, all you'll need to do is drop the pieces into place. If you put the insulation in first, you'll have to work around it when you are working with the plywood. Don't try it. Make the plywood fit first. You'll be making a big mistake if you put the insulation down first. More about why later.

The first step to correctly fitting plywood to the floor is a simple one. Take one of the sheets of plywood (uncut) and position it between the two rear wheel wells so that it is in the van as shown in Fig. 3-2. The edge should come within an inch of either wheel well. Screw this piece down in two places to hold it throughout the rest of the procedure. Use the drill and screwdriver attachment. (First start the screw with an ordinary screwdriver. Then, using the drill, drive it the rest of the way. You may have to use an 1/8-in. drill bit to make a hole in the metal floor.) But be wary of the location of the gas tank. More than one unwary converter has drilled right into to the top of it. So before you drill any holes, check the gas tank

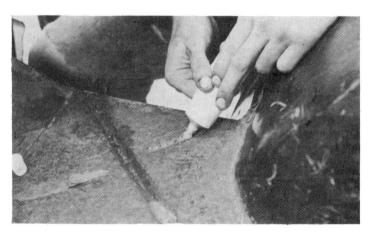

Fig. 3-1. The first step in installing the floor is to fill in any holes with silicone sealant. Avoid using too much sealant. It only takes a little to do the job and using more than necessary is just a waste of money.

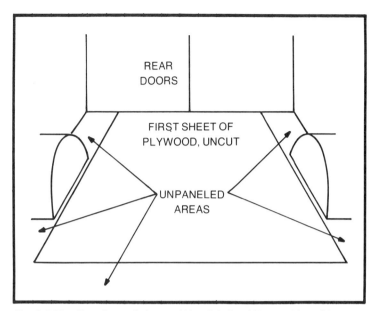

Fig. 3-2. The first sheet of plywood (4′ × 8′) should be positioned between the wheel wells and against the rear doors as shown.

location and make sure you have adequate clearance for the drill bit. A couple of screws in the forward end of the plywood should be enough to hold it still. Remember, before drilling through the floor, check the underside for gas lines, brake lines, exhaust pipes, and gas tanks.

With the first piece of plywood firmly anchored in place, the next step is to cover the bare floor surrounding it. The necessary steps will vary from van to van but the principle is the same. Don't cut the plywood into strange shapes to try to fit it into place. You should be able to cover the entire floor with nothing but rectangular pieces as shown in Fig. 3-3. Select an area where a rectangular piece of plywood will fit. Measure its width and length carefully, then cut a piece to fit that spot. There's no need for the plywood to fit around ribs found on the walls of a van. It should extend to the rib and no farther. The area between the edge of the plywood and the side of the van will be hidden by a wall that is installed later. Also, don't spend too much time trying to make the cuts super straight. Just get the pieces to fit roughly into place. The layers to follow will hide any mistakes you make at this point unless they are really drastic. Be sure to allow enough room for all the doors to close properly. This is a mistake I made the first time I remodeled a van. I cut the plywood to cover the *entire* floor and didn't allow any room for the doors to close. I ended up doing a lot of filing (Fig. 3-4). Allow approximately 3 in. of clearance for the doors.

Don't let the wheel wells scare you. It's not hard to fit plywood around them. Figure 3-5 shows just how simple it is. In fact, the wheel wells require no special attention. They'll be taken care of if you cover the rest of the floor using the

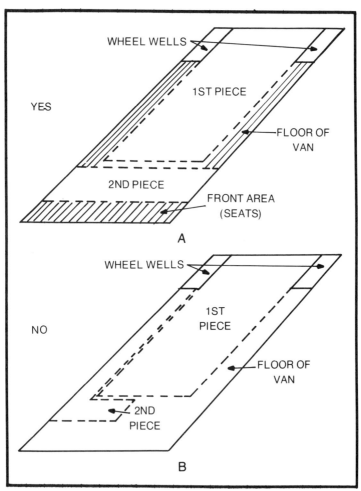

Fig. 3-3. Try to work with rectangular pieces only. The job will go much more quickly. Cutting the pieces to strange shapes usually wastes more time than it saves.

Fig. 3-4. If not enough room is allowed for the closing of the doors, you may end up doing some filling as was done here. The edge of the floor panel had to be filed down until the door could close completely.

procedure outlined. Remember the floor should not extend any farther forward than the mounting holes for the two front seats. To take the floor all the way forward would involve cutting the plywood to fit around the engine cover, gas pedal, brake pedal, and all other immovable obstructions. This is a difficult task, to say the least, and requires a special procedure for each van. Stop the floor at the back of the seats.

Once you've cut the second piece of plywood to fit areas surrounding the first piece, remove all the plywood and put it aside. Remember where each piece goes. It'll be similar to a jigsaw puzzle when it comes time to replace them. With the second layer ready to go in, you're ready to install the insulation.

Laying The Insulation

This is the most difficult step you'll encounter when installing a floor. If you've ever worked with fiberglass insulation, you know why. If you haven't, you're in for an experience. Fiberglass insulation should be handled with *gloves*. You should wear long jeans and a long-sleeve shirt also. The reason is simple: if the fiberglass touches your skin, it'll make you itch. Tiny fibers of glass from the insulation work their way into your skin causing an itching discomfort. So before you even touch the fiberglass, don some protective clothing. You may think I am exaggerating, but I've been there. Once the fiberglass touches an area of your skin, the itching starts. But it doesn't confine itself to that spot. It spreads. If you scratch, it gets worse and continues to spread. The only thing you can do is wait for it to pass. But if you take the time to dig up some clothing that will offer adequate protection, you won't regret it. You can now see why the plywood is cut to size first, and then the insulation is installed. This step can be mildly unpleasant or it can be an ordeal. Don't make it the latter. Here are a few guidelines when working with fiberglass insulation:

- Avoid unnecessary fiberglass movement. Decide where you want it and put it there. When it is handled, little pieces of fiberglass break off and go into the air. This is better avoided!
- Avoid contacting the fiberglass with your bare skin.
- Work in a well-ventilated area. You've probably heard this before and it is a good idea.
- Install the insulation with the paper side *up*. The reason for this is obvious. The paper acts as a barrier between you and the fiberglass.

If you follow these four simple rules, you should be able to get through the insulation step with a minimum of discomfort.

To cut the insulation to size, use a pair of scissors. Measure the length of the floor and cut two pieces of insulation

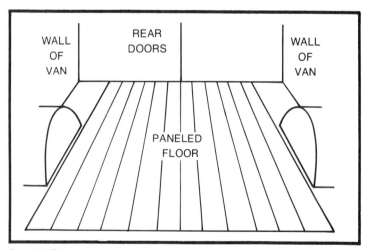

Fig. 3-5. The wheel wells should not worry you. When the entire floor is paneled and covered, the cut around the wheel wells will be completely hidden.

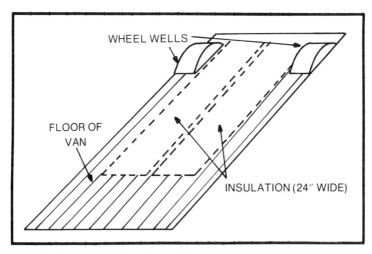

Fig. 3-6. First, two strips of insulation are positioned between the two wheel wells. They should extend as far forward as necessary to cover the floor area that will later be covered with plywood.

to that size. Lay them lengthwise in the van between the two rear wheel wells as shown in Fig. 3-6. Cut two more strips to fit into the areas along the walls (Fig. 3-7). Cover any other bare areas where the plywood will go.

The insulation must be held into place while the plywood is installed. A few two-by-fours acting as weights will be ideal for

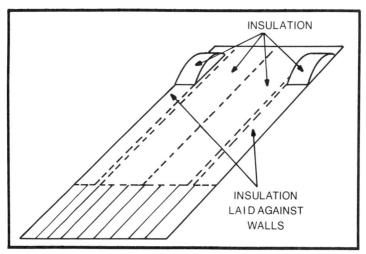

Fig. 3-7. Two strips of insulation are layed along the bottoms of the walls. The insulation will be held in place with the plywood flooring.

this purpose. They can be laid across the insulation and left until the plywood is in place. They can then be removed; the plywood will hold the insulation in place.

Once the insulation is cut to size and is covering the floor, you're ready to install the second layer—the plywood.

Laying The Plywood

Very carefully, take the uncut piece of plywood and position it as it was before—between the two rear wheel wells and extending forward. Then remove the weights from under the plywood that were used to hold the insulation in place. Now, using the drill and the screwdriver bit, fasten the plywood to the floor. If possible, line up the two holes in the plywood with the two holes you drilled in the floor to hold the piece in place the first time. (This may be pretty difficult since the fiberglass is covering the floor. If you can't line up the holes, they'll need to be patched from the underside of the van.) Install screws about a foot apart over the entire surface of the plywood. Don't worry about using too many. You can't. Once the first piece of plywood is secured, place the remaining pieces in their respective positions and fasten them to the floor in the same fashion. Pay special attention to the seams. Try to make adjacent pieces line up as well as possible as in Fig. 3-8.

Once the plywood has been screwed into place over the insulation, you can sit back and see that you've accomplished something. You now have a clean, level surface to work on throughout the rest of the remodeling process. You also have a built-in scratch pad. If you need to make a note or jot down a

Fig. 3-8. When installing the floor panels, try to keep the crack formed between them as even as possible. Avoid overtorqueing the screws since warping will result.

measurement, the floor is an ideal place to do so. It doesn't matter how marked up the floor gets; it will be covered with carpeting and no one will ever know.

Two layers remain to be installed to complete the floor—the padding and the carpet. But these layers should not be installed until all the interior work has been completed. If the padding and the carpet are installed now, they may be damaged. Sawdust, glue, and dirty tools can damage the carpet. So it's best to keep the carpet in a safe place until it can be installed without the danger of ruin. Installation of padding and carpet is always one of the last steps in the remodeling process.

Okay. That takes care of phase one. The floor is installed. You have a long way to go yet before your van even looks as though it's being converted, but the floor is a good start. Next, the sound system is considered.

Chapter 4

The Sound System

This chapter may seem out of place following the chapter on the installation of the floor but it is here for a reason. Decisions must be made that will affect the following chapters, so it is necessary to deal with the selection and purchase of the sound system now.

The special wiring necessary for a great sound system is discussed here.

CASSETTE OR CARTRIDGE?

When deciding what tape deck to buy, you are faced with the immediate question of whether to go 8-track or cassette. For the last ten years much has been said in favor of both. Some people are diehard fans of one system while the other system attracts its own group of followers. The cartridge system uses a plastic case housing a continuous loop of recorded tape as shown in Fig. 4-1. The cartridge will play continuously when inserted in the deck. There are four *programs* to choose from. Each program consists of two channels—left and right. Two channels times four programs equals eight tracks. Hence, the term 8-track. When the channel button is pushed, the tape head assumes a higher position relative to the tape and makes contact with a different portion of it. In this way, the head sees a totally different signal. When the channel button is pushed again, the head is raised another

Fig. 4-1. In a cartridge, the tape pulls out of the center of the spool and winds on the outer edge of it. The resulting drag on the tape is tremendous.

notch and sees yet another program. This can be done four times. After the fourth program has played, the head automatically returns to the first program.

A cassette uses the reel-to-reel principle with a tape containing four tracks. A supply spool and a take-up spool are housed in a plastic case as in Fig. 4-2. As the tape travels through the cassette, the supply spool empties and the take-up spool fills. When the supply spool is completely empty, the cassette must be either turned over to play the other two tracks or the tape must be rewound. This system works the same way as the reel-to-reel machines designed for professional and home use.

The cassette, as we said, is a four track system. The tape head sees two *tracks* in one direction and then, when the tape is turned over, the head plays the other two tracks, making a total of four tracks.

Advantages exist for both modes of sound reproduction. For instance, a cartridge will play continuously as long as it is left in the deck whereas a cassette system will eventually come to the end of the tape and stop (provided the deck is not the more expensive automatic reversing unit). More about this later. Cartridges are currently more common than cassettes, so there is a slightly wider selection of prerecorded material available. However, cassettes have some advantages of their

65

own. They are about one-third the size of cartridges, so three times as many can be stored in the same amount of space. This is particularly advantageous when dealing with tape systems for vehicles where space is limited. Another advantage is that quality cassettes are more reliable. Cartridges have a tendency to foul up. If you've ever owned a cartridge deck before, you've probably experienced that feeling of futility when your deck eats a tape and you don't know why. Chances are that it wasn't you're fault. It was probably due to the inherent design deficiencies in the cartridge. There is a tremendous amount of friction on the tape as it pulls out of the center of the spool (Fig. 4-1) and winds on the outer edge. Well made cassettes can have few such problems if the separate spools for takeup and feed (Fig. 4-2) are a low friction design.

The cassette has the added advantage of being capable of rapid tape movement in either direction. The cartridge, because of its design, is mechanically incapable of being rewound. It can only go forward. Some cartridge decks are equipped with a fast-forward feature but is is still quite slow and moves no faster than the recording speed of professional tape recorders. Most cartridge decks with this feature move the tape at only two to four times the playing speed which is 3 3/4-in. per second. That means that the cartridge is traveling at 7 1/2 to 15 inches per second. But the cassette system can

Fig. 4-2. A cassette works in the same way as a reel-to-reel machine. One spool feeds the tape and the other takes up the tape.

move the tape in either direction up to twenty times as fast as the 1 7/8-in. playing speed. A cartridge system works in such a way that as long as the cartridge is in the deck, the tape is in contact with the head. But a cassette system lifts the head away from the tape in the fast-forward mode. So tape head wear is eliminated during fast forward or fast reverse.

Another area where cassettes beat out cartridges is in the amount of music that can be contained on a single tape. Cartridges are seldom longer than one hour. But cassettes are available that play for two hours. This means that the cassette doesn't have to be changed as often as the cartridge. And they take up less space.

So far all the advantages and disadvantages mentioned are practical ones. But one area remains to be covered. And it is the most important factor when deciding between cassette and cartridge. Which one sounds better? Most people who have critically listened to both types of tape systems will tell you that the cassette system sounds significantly better than the cartridge systems available today. But the real test is to listen and compare them yourself. You make the decision of which sounds better. Find a friend that has a vehicular cassette system and ask for a demonstration. Then do the same with the cartridge system. A simple comparison should be enough for you to form your own conclusion. It was enough for me. Upon hearing cassettes, I have never been satisfied with the way cartridge systems sound. The cassette system is such a vast improvement, in my opinion, that I believe cartridges are on the way out.

STEREO OR QUAD?

The decision of whether to get a cassette or cartridge system is primary when shopping for a tape deck. But recently a new controversy has surfaced. Should the system be stereo or quad?

Since its onset, the topic of quadraphonic sound has been the subject of a raging controversy between the die-hard stereo fans and the explorers. Some have said that quad is a ripoff or a hoax. It's up to you to decide if quad is worth the extra expense.

There are several ways to reproduce quad, or 4-channel sound, but they all fall into one of two categories—true or "discrete" quad and "synthesized" quad. A discrete system employs four separate channels of information where a synthesized system derives two of the channels (the rear channels) from the other two (the front channels). If you decide to go with the discrete system you will be forced to go with the cartridge system for the simple reason that there are no discrete cassette systems available due primarily to legal restrictions imposed by Phillips, the inventor of the cassette system used today. But discrete cartridge systems are available. They have the same number of tracks, but only half as many programs.

Another alternative is synthesized quad. By using what is called a *matrix*, quad can be simulated with surprising results. In fact, you would be hard-pressed to tell the difference between a good matrix system and a discrete system. I have a synthesized quad system in my van and it is quite acceptable. The two rear channels of a synthesized quad system are fed a partially out of phase program when compared with the front channels. This creates the four-channel effect.

Fortunately for the consumer, the decision to go quad will cost little more than a similar stereo unit. Cassette decks employing a built-in matrix are available for only slightly more than their stereo counterpart. Cartridge discrete decks are generally about 25 percent more expensive than a similar stereo deck.

FEATURES

The three basic controls you should be concerned with are tone, volume, and balance. These controls will be used more than any others.

Tone Controls

First of all, not all tone controls are alike; it's important to know what's available, and how they work. Probably the most basic tone control currently being installed on decks is the simple switch. It is usually marked "hi" and "lo" and sometimes has a neutral position in the middle. If more treble is desired, the switch is placed in the "hi" position. Similarily, if the bass is lacking, the switch is set to "lo." This system is extremely basic for all it really does is attenuate the treble. It doesn't actually "boost" the base. The user has very little choice in how much treble or bass is attenuated. A much better system is the slide bar (Fig. 4-3). This arrangement gives the

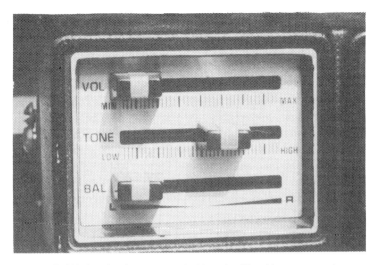

Fig. 4-3. A slide bar for the tone control is a significant improvement over a simple switch. In this way the tone can be varied extensively whereas a switch is preset and varies the tone only slightly. A slide bar tone control is not as good as independent bass and trebel controls but it is the second best approach to the problem.

user greater control over the frequency range of the tone circuit. Instead of a preset treble cast, as with a switch, the user can apply increasingly greater or lesser amounts of tone control action. Unfortunately, while this system is a vast improvement over the simple switch and can sometimes even include bass boost circuitry, it is still not ideal. It suffers from one major drawback—the bass and treble cannot be independently controlled. The user is forced to make a choice between more bass and less treble or more treble with less bass. He can't have both. The ideal system would allow the treble to be varied without affecting the bass. A separate control for each function would allow this. Decks are available with this type of tone control system but they are the more expensive. Such tone control systems are almost unheard of on units costing below $200. Unless you have the extra cash to pay for the more expensive units, settle for the slide bar type tone control (or rotating knob type; the effect is the same). It is certainly a big improvement over the simple switch.

Balance Controls

Again, there are two basic types of balance control available. One type is incorporated into the volume control.

The system consists of two knobs or sliding bars (Fig. 4-4). These are simply two volume controls, one for the left and right channels respectively. This system is effective, but it is unnecessarily awkward. The balance cannot be adjusted without affecting the volume. Likewise, if the volume is increased, the balance must be readjusted. The improved system works like this: as the left channel volume is increased, the right channel volume is decreased by the same amount. With this system the balance can be adjusted using only one control, usually a slide bar or knob (Fig. 4-5). The volume can also be adjusted without affecting the balance setting. This system is particularly advantageous on a deck designed for vehicular use simply because it is simple. The simpler the controls the better.

Volume Controls

A third control is common to all decks; it is the volume control. Some units incorporate the volume control into the balance controls. Others use an independent control. Of course, the independent type is easier to use and is more effective.

Tape Transport

In addition to the three controls already mentioned, one area remains that should be of concern to the prospective buyer: the tape transport. If you have already decided to go with a cartridge system, you have little choice. There is only

Fig. 4-4. A split balance control is incorporated into the volume control. This arrangement is far less desirable than the single slide bar.

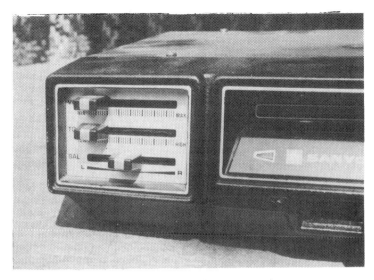

Fig. 4-5. A slide bar for the balance control gives all the control that is necessary and is much easier to use than the split balance type.

one system available. A fast-forward control system as shown in Fig. 4-6. Your only choice in the matter is whether the fast-forward is the locking type. If the control does not lock, you'll have to hold the fast-forward control in place as long as you want the tape to be moved rapidly. If you want to hear a

Fig. 4-6. The only tape transport control available on cartridge decks is a fast-forward control; and it is usually very inadequate.

song at the end of the tape and you're at the beginning, you must hold the control in place until the desired location is reached. With a locking control, the switch is simply set to fast-forward.

But if you've opted for a cassette system, your transport mechanism choices are numerous. The best movement control available on cassette decks is one that allows fast-forward as well as rewind (Fig. 4-7). All *cassettes* are capable of rapid tape movement in either direction, but not all decks have the capability. Some cassette decks have only a fast-forward control. The ideal tape control system is one that allows rapid tape movement in either direction as well as a locking system so the control doesn't have to be held in place. The control should lock in rewind as well as fast-forward. This type of mechanism gives the user maximum control over the tape movement. He can now effectively search for a particular song he wants to hear. If he overshoots the mark in fast-forward, he simply rewinds the tape a little. It's clear that his system is a big improvement over one that allows rapid tape movement in only one direction.

Automatic Reversing

A handy feature available on cassette decks is called *automatic reversing*. Instead of the machine playing one side and stopping, it reverses the direction of play when it comes to the end of the tape, thus eliminating the need to flip the tape over to play the second program (Fig. 4-8). This system eliminates the last major drawback of cassette decks. A tape can be inserted and it will play continuously until it is

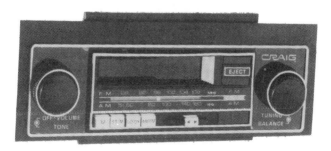

Fig. 4-7. Because of the design of the cassette, rapid tape movement is possible in either direction and many decks take advantage of this fact. This Craig unit is capable of both fast-forward and rewind. (Courtesy of Craig Enterprises.)

Fig. 4-8. This automatic-reversing unit by Uher is one of the best on the market. It is packed with incredible features and is billed as "the world's smallest portable high-fidelity cassette deck." The frequency response is an incredible 25 to 15,000 Hz., the best I've ever heard of any cassette deck this small. (Courtesy of Uher of America Inc.)

removed. You enjoy continuous sound with this handy feature. Also, the deck can be made to reverse direction of play on demand, so the other program is always at your fingertips.

The automatic reversing feature is quite a luxury. But it suffers from one major drawback—it's finicky. The automatic reverse mechanism adds many more parts to the deck; just that many more parts that can fail. And they sometimes do. The machine may stop reversing one day for no apparent reason, or it may start taking longer and longer to reverse. What it boils down to is this. You'll have to pay the price for the pleasure of having both programs at your fingertips: reliability and cost. The question is how much this feature is worth to you. Automatic reversing units are available that are extremely high quality (Fig. 4-8), but unfortunately, they are very high-priced. A modestly priced automatic-reversing deck, if it is treated properly, will give lots of service. *But it must be treated properly.* Inexpensive decks cannot stand the strain of rigorous treatment. It'll need to be properly cleaned frequently. In short, you'll have to pamper it—for example, not use it in extremely hot or cold environments.

Automatic Shutoff

A feature called *automatic shutoff* is available on cartridge and cassette decks. On an automatic reversing cassette deck, this means that the deck will play both programs of the tape and then eject it if the auto-stop switch is engaged. On a non-automatic reversing deck the one program is played and then the cassette is ejected. A cartridge deck will play the tape and then eject it. With either style, the automatic stop feature is a wise investment. It can save lots of wear-and-tear on your tape deck. Some cassette decks will run to the end of the tape and not shut off. The motors keep trying to turn the cassette but they can't because the tape has run out. The cassette holds the motors still while they are trying to turn. You can imagine what effect this has on the internal parts of the deck. Wear is drastically increased. In fact, if the deck is left in this stage overnight, it could be ruined. So the automatic-stop feature is something that is worth the extra money whether you go with an automatic-reversing unit or not.

Special Features

There are lots of little features that are available on tape decks that may interest you. Some decks have built-in tape counters. With this feature, specific places on the tape can be found easily. Some decks have built-in recorders (Fig. 4-8). Still others have end-of-tape lights and a built-in battery source.

To this point I have dealt with tape decks only. But some units incorporate a radio with a basic deck (Fig. 4-9). Anything from plain AM to stereo FM reception is available, all at varying prices. The built-in AM radio will cost slightly more than the basic deck. The FM stereo reception will cost you lots more. It's a nice feature but manufacturers overrate its importance and charge excessively for it. A big advantage to getting a deck with a built-in radio is that the factory radio in the van can now be removed and the deck can be installed in its place to provide you with a very professional in-dash installation without losing a radio. Usually the most the job will require is a slight modification of the dash. Check to see

Fig. 4-9. For the person interested in an "entertainment center" Craig markets this unit which includes an AM-FM radio as well as an automatic-reversing cassette deck. (Courtesy of Craig Enterprises.)

Fig. 4-10a. An in-dash installation looks very much like a factory-installed radio. This fact alone is good insurance against theft. A unit mounted in the dash is much more difficult to steal than one mounted under it.

that the deck will fit before buying. Sometimes a special "installation kit" is available for specific makes and models of vans.

MOUNTING

Tape decks are designed to be mounted in two ways—in the dash or under it (Fig. 4-10). If you'd like the deck installed in the dash, the factory radio can be replaced, or a new hole can be cut for the deck. The trouble with this latter method is finding a place that will accept the deck. If you're going to

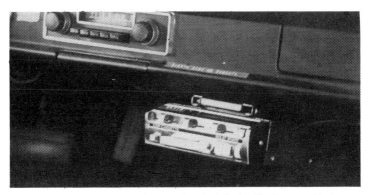

Fig. 4-10b. A deck mounted under the dash looks like it was added as an after-thought and is much easier to steal. Thieves look for units mounted like this.

replace the radio with your deck, the easiest way to go is to get a ruler and measure the dimensions. You may have to search for quite a while to get a deck that will fit the confines of your dash opening, but the finished result will be very pleasing. Nothing looks more professional than a deck built right into the dash. It's out of the way and difficult to steal. Unfortunately, many times the tape deck will not fit where the radio does. So you'll have to find an alternate plan.

You can still make the installation look very professional if you exercise a little creativity. Most people, after ruling out the possibility of dash-mounting their deck, would mount it under the dash. It can look unprofessional. The deck looks as though it was added as a afterthought. So, think about mounting the deck on the ceiling. Mounted here, the deck is out of the way and, more importantly, out of sight from would-be thieves. I mounted my deck this way and found that people riding with me would inevitably ask where the deck was mounted. They seldom looked up at the ceiling.

Put the deck wherever you like. Don't feel bound by convention. If you think it looks good mounted under the front seat, put it there. Concern yourself with finding a spot that is safe for the deck. It should be a place relatively free of dust, clumsy feet, and crooks. The dust will increase internal wear, so consider it an enemy. If you can find a place that meets these requirements you've found a good place to mount your deck. For instance, the glove compartment is a popular mounting place. As far as security is concerned, it is ideal if the compartment can be locked. The glove compartment is free of moisture, dust, and clumsy feet, making it pretty close to the ideal. It sometimes makes the operation of the deck a little inconvenient from the driver's seat, though.

SPECIFICATIONS

When tape decks are packaged to be sold, the manufacturer includes what are called "specifications" (Fig. 4-11). These tell you the capabilities of that particular machine. To shop for a deck intelligently, it is necessary to interpret these specifications.

The primary specification to be concerned with is *frequency response*. All decks have different capabilities as far as frequency response is concerned. This is partially why

RECORDING: 2 track stereo Philips system

CASSETTE: C30, C46, C60, C90, C120

TAPE SPEED: 1-7/8 IPS – 4.7 cms

FREQUENCY RANGE: 25–15,000 ± 2 dB

SIGNAL-TO-NOISE RATIO (RMS A curve): ≧ 56 dB

WOW AND FLUTTER (RMS): ≦ ± 0.12% (maximum)

ERASURE: ≧ 70 dB

OPERATING MODES: Mono & stereo – recording & playback

SOLID STATE DEVICES: 33 transistors, 1 Darlington, 2 FET transistors, 30 diodes, 2 IC final stages (monolithic integrated circuit)

OUTPUT POWER: Battery operated 2 x 1 W (continuous power), power supply-operated 2 x 1.3 W (continuous power)

INPUTS: Microphone 0.2mV - 200mV/500 Ohm, radio 4mV-550mV/47K Ohm, phono 150mV-15V/1M Ohm

OUTPUTS: Radio/ampl. ≧ 500 mV across 15K Ohm, external 2 x 2 V across 4 Ohm (battery-operated), speaker 2 x 2.3 V across 4 Ohm (power supply-operated)

MICROPHONE: Built-in condenser microphone (low-voltage technology – **not an electret system)**

AUTOMATIC REVERSE: Automatic photo-sensitive electronic control of tape direction in playback mode (continuous)

MOTOR: Electronically regulated wear-resistant DC motor (no commutator)

AUTOMATIC LEVEL CONTROL: Disconnectable FET system

REMOTE CONTROL: Start/stop and selection of tape run direction

AUTOMATIC SHUT-OFF: In record mode, fast forward and rewind modes

POWER SUPPLY: 6 "C" cell 1.5V special rechargeable batteries, car batteries 12V, power supply unit 100-130V, 200-240V AC, 50 and 60 Hz – the power supply unit acts simultaneously as an automatic charger for the rechargeable batteries

COUNTER: 3-digit

DIMENSIONS (width x height x depth): approximately 7 x 2 x 7 inches

WEIGHT: Approximately 4-1/2 lbs.

All values measured at a battery voltage of 8V

Fig. 4-11. These specifications are for the Uher CR 210 pictured in Fig. 4-8 and they are far better than most decks on the market. Be sure to examine the specs of the unit you are considering buying carefully before making any decision. The frequency response, wow and flutter specifications, and signal-to-noise ratio are the most important specs of all.

all decks sound different. The frequency response figures tell you the *maximum frequency range of that unit*. This specification is rated in *cycles per second*. Every tone or "frequency" vibrates at a set number of cycles-per-second. Low notes vibrate very slowly while high notes vibrate very quickly. The rate of vibration is called *hertz*. If a unit is said to be capable of reproducing 40 hertz notes, it means that if you were to record a tone that vibrates 40 times in one second, and play it back on that deck, it would be able to electrically reproduce it. A typical car tape deck specification for frequency response is 40 hertz to 10,000 hertz. A machine with these specifications can reproduce a note that vibrates at least 40 times in one second and no more than 10,000 times in one second. As long as the note falls between these two rates of vibration, the deck can reproduce, or convert it, to an electrical signal.

But tape decks don't reproduce all notes equally well. Some decks can reproduce a 2000 hertz note better than they can reproduce a 5000 hertz note. For this reason, the frequency response specification will usually include a plus or minus figure in decibels. Some manufacturers include a graph showing the frequency characteristics of that unit in addition to the plus or minus decibel figure (Fig. 4-12). This tells you the degree of variation that particular deck has between notes within its frequency range. For instance, if a deck has a response of 40 hertz to 10,000 hertz plus or minus 3 decibels, the maximum deviation between any two notes within the frequency range is six decibels. The decibel unit is a way of rating volume. So a plus or minus of three decibels means that no frequency will be more than six decibels louder than any other frequency unless they are different in the original recording. A plus or minus figure of 3 is probably the best you'll see when shopping for a deck unless you are checking a particularly high-priced unit. The maximum frequency response you're likely to encounter is in the vicinity of 30 to 12,000 hertz (abbreviated Hz.) Decks are available with specs that far exceed these, but unfortunately, they are very expensive. One unit I've seen has a frequency response of 30 to 17,000. This is as good as most home cassette systems. The plus or minus decibel figure was only two. That's a significant improvement over the less expensive units. A home-type deck with specs like that could cost as much as $1900. The lowest priced one I've seen was nearly $300.

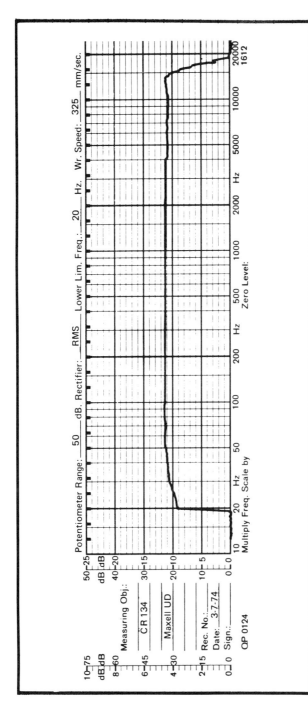

Fig. 4-12. A curve shows the frequency response much more effectively than do numbers. This curve is for the Uher CR 210 and is impressively flat. The deck drops off at 20 Hz at the low end and 15,000 Hz at the high end. You're unlikely to run across specs this good unless you're shopping among really expensive units, but this arrangement of showing the frequency response of a unit is very useful regardless of the quality of that unit. (Courtesy Uher of America.)

Another specification that is certainly worth considering is wow and flutter. The ideal cassette deck should move the tape at a constant speed of 1 7/8 inches per second. A cartridge deck should move the tape at precisely 3 3/4 ips. There should be absolutely no deviation. That deck doesn't exist, however. So to give the consumer an idea of how well a deck will approach the ideal, manufacturers include a wow and flutter specification. The lower the percentage of wow and flutter the better.

If you include a radio with your tape deck, there is a specification that you're likely to run into. *Sensitivity*. Rated in microvolts, this specification tells you how well the radio responds to an incoming signal. It's a little misleading though, because the specs given are usually deficient. For instance, a common sensitivity rating for a car radio is five microvolts. That means that an incoming signal must have a signal strength of at least five microvolts for the radio to receive it. This doesn't mean that that signal will be listenable. It only means that it can be heard. So in itself the sensitivity rating is meaningless. The best way to check the sensitivity of a radio is to listen to it. Find a weak station and see how well the radio receives it.

The final specification to be considered is power output. Tape decks are rated for power in *watts-per-channel*. There are two types of rating: IHF (Institute of High Fidelity) and rms. The IHF rating will always be much higher than the rms rating because it measures *peak power*. The rms rating however, measures *continuous power*. For instance, if a deck is said to put out five watts per channel IHF, the five watts is a peak reading. The deck does not put out a steady five watts per channel. But if the rating is five watts per channel rms, the deck puts out a continuous five watts per channel. The rms value is the truer rating. An IHF rating makes the specs look good for a tape deck. When the consumer looks at specs and sees a deck that puts out 20 watts per channel IHF as opposed to a deck that puts out 15 watts per channel rms, he will probably choose the former. But if you understand the rating system used, you will be able to make an intelligent selection based on the analysis of all the pertinent specifications. This is our ultimate goal. By discussing these different specifications you are no longer at the mercy of the salesman. You are equipped with an understanding of what the figures mean.

When concerning yourself with power, be careful not to overemphasize its importance. Five watts per channel is not much if the unit is to be used in your home, but in a van, it is a powerhouse.

The last test when deciding on which tape deck to buy is a listening test! You try a van before you buy it: this is the all-important test. It's the same with a tape deck. Take a tape you know to be recorded well, and use it as a demonstration tape. Compare the different machines and listen for yourself which sounds better. Try the features. If you wnat an automatic-reversing unit, test one. Find a place that will give you personal attention and will let you listen to the deck *before* you buy.

SPEAKERS

When buying speakers, you should rely on one thing—your ear. Get what sounds good to you. This should be the primary criterion when making your speaker selection. All other determinants are subordinate to this one. You are buying the speaker to listen to, so it stands to reason that *that* should be the acid test for your selection. However, to help you get an idea of what any one speaker is capable of, some manufacturers include frequency specifications. It is calculated the same way it is for tape decks. The same rules apply. The broader the frequency range, the better. The lower the plus-or-minus decibel figure, the better.

There are several points worth mentioning in addition. Figure 4-13 shows the various parts of a typical speaker. I will be referring to this figure in the next few paragraphs.

Notice the hinge of the speaker in Fig. 4-13. This supports the cone and allows it to travel forward and backward very rapidly on the coil, thus creating sound. This hinge should be made of some material other than paper. Cloth is used in most speakers, and it works quite well. It lasts longer than paper. It is more nimble. And it is less susceptible to the damaging effects of humidity. Some speakers use various synthetic materials to accomplish the same result.

They are not any worse than cloth, but in the world of mobile audio, it is doubtful they are any better either. So don't pay extra for it. And steer clear of speakers with paper hinges. This type wears out sooner than the cloth hinge and is not so moisture-resistant. Naturally, you'll find the paper hinge on the cheaper speakers.

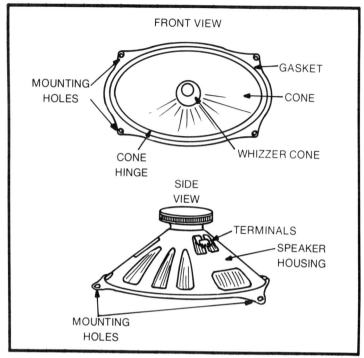

Fig. 4-13. The names of the various parts of a speaker are all self-evident with the exception of the whizzer cone.

Some speakers have whizzer cones (Fig. 4-13). These are usually made of plastic or paper. There is no advantage to either material. The whizzer cone enhances the upper mid- and high-frequency characteristics of the speaker and therefore is usually a desirable feature.

POWER HANDLING

The best way to tell how much power a speaker will handle is to check the specs. There is a common myth that the larger the magnet, the more power the speaker can handle and the better the speaker. This is not necessarily true. While some very good speakers use large magnets, many cheap speakers do also. A speaker with a large magnet may not handle much power at all. That magnet could have been put on by the manufacturer to help sell the speaker. The manufacturer is aware that people think a larger magnet is better, so he takes advantage of it by putting a larger magnet on the speaker, to

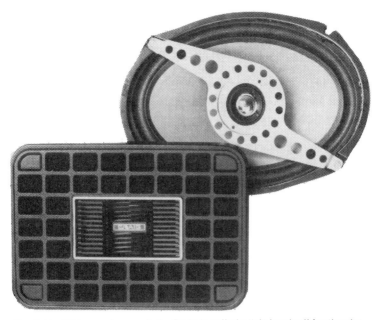

Fig. 4-14a. This speaker made by Craig is called a "six by nine" for the simple reason that it is six inches wide and nine inches long. Designed to be flush-mounted, it is no more difficult to install than a round speaker. (Courtesy of Craig Enterprises.)

boost sales. If specs are unavailable, there is another way to determine how much power a speaker will handle. While you won't be able to get an exact wattage rating, you can get a general idea of how much power the speaker will handle without damage.

Fig. 4-14b. Speakers come in several shapes. This one made by Jensen is designed to be surface-mounted but can, with slight modification, be flush-mounted. (Courtesy of Jensen Laboratories.)

Examine the actual coil diameter. The larger the coil the more power the speaker can handle. Compare the coil size of a speaker with a large magnet to the coil size of a speaker with a small magnet. If the coil diameters are the same, you may assume that the speakers can handle equal power input.

Speakers come in several shapes (Fig. 4-14). However, the shape of the speaker is only important in the installation step.

Fig. 4-15a. Sometimes a surface-mount installation is the only possible arrangement as it was here where the wall was not thick enough to accommodate this particular speaker. When a flush-mount design is not possible, it is necessary to find a container to hold the speaker. A black box has been used here but there are many more possibilities that exist that are much more attractive. For instance you might use a short piece of ceramic pipe as the speaker enclosure and cover the top with a fabric like burlap so the sound can get through.

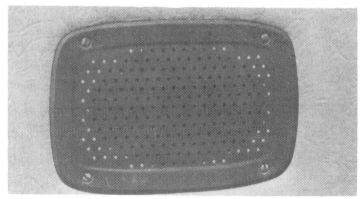

Fig. 4-15b. A flush-mount speaker is infinitely preferable to a surface-mount installation. This speaker is mounted in the door; it is out of the way completely, held securely, and looks nicer than a surface-mount type.

The conditions in your van may make the oval speaker the easiest to install. Or a round one may fit better. As to the type of installation you choose to use, there are two ways to go. The speaker can be flush-mounted or surface mounted. I don't believe a surface-mount installation looks very professional. It looks much better to flush-mount them and get them out of the way permanently. They are less conspicuous when mounted this way and are more easily incorporated into individual design schemes. Figure 4-15 shows examples of both types of installations.

Finally, it is necessary to decide where everything will be mounted. Speakers and the tape or radio deck should be positioned before any actual cutting is done. It shouldn't take long for you to decide where everything is to go. Put them where they look good to you, but remember to be absolutely correct, don't place stereo speakers so they face each other. They should face you. I know this rule is violated even in factory installations, but if you want the best system (in theory anyway) mount both the left and right channel speakers on the same surface or place. Once you've decided where to place the speakers, next step is to deal with the wiring.

The only work covered in this chapter is the *special* wiring needed if you include a sound system in your van. The speaker and tape deck installation is covered in other chapters. For instance, speaker installation in walls is covered in the chapter on wall installation.

WIRING

Although the following chapter covers the total electrical wiring picture, it is necessary to cover special sound system wiring here. Depending on the placement of the speakers and the type of deck you'll be mounting, the wiring will vary. If you are going to install a cassette deck and include a four channel matrix decoder system, Fig. 4-16 shows how it's done. If the deck has a built-in matrix, the instruction book that came with the deck will fully explain simple wiring procedures.

At this stage, the rear of your van consists of lots of bare metal and a nice wood floor. In this wiring step, the wires are run for all the speakers and the tape deck.

The best kind to use is ordinary lamp, or zip, cord. It's commonly available at most hardware stores and it's pretty cheap. The wire should be 16 gauge, ideally, but the lighter 18 gauge is acceptable. The higher the number, the thinner the wire. Naturally, the cost changes with the gauge. As the number goes up, the price goes down. Twenty gauge wire is cheaper than 16 gauge wire. If the speaker wires will be short, say from the deck in the dash to a front door, you could get away with 20 gauge wire. But it is not wise to skimp at this point. If the wire is too thin, it will have a high resistance; it will not carry the audio power to the speaker efficiently. It could cause a loss of volume, and distortion when the volume is only slightly turned up. If the wires to speakers will be long, like to the rear doors, the thicker wire is a necessity. For, the longer the wire, the harder it is for the signal to get through. So if the wires must be very long, you must compensate by using a heavier wire.

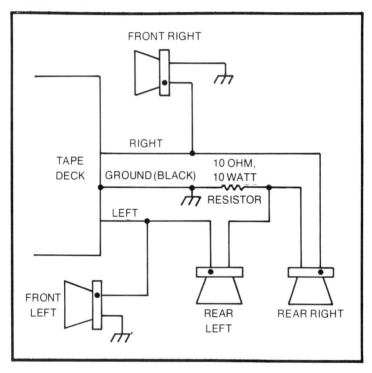

Fig. 4-16. Including a four-channel matrix in your sound system can really make a big difference. The two rear channels are synthesized from the two front, via a resistor. The rear channel negative leads come from one side of the resistor instead of ground. The positive leads connect to the positive leads of the front channels.

Here's a time when you can save yourself lots of trouble. Get lamp cord that has *clear* insulation. Some places sell it as speaker wire specifically. The insulation, instead of brown, gray, or black, is clear. The two wires running through it are usually aluminum. When you're doing all the wiring for the speakers, you must observe correct polarity. Speaker polarity is indicated by a dot at one terminal. If you connect one end of the wire to a positive, or marked with a dot, speaker terminal, the other end must also be connected to a positive terminal. Likewise for the negative wire. Keeping this straight can be difficult with brown or black wire. But with clear wire, it's a snap. Just connect the copper lead to positive at both ends. The aluminum is then used for ground or negative. Simple. Don't underestimate the importance of maintaining consistent polarity. If you are using a four channel matrix, it is particularly important. Speaker systems connected out of phase are noted for a lack of bass response. The low (base) sounds from out-of-phase speakers tend to cancel themselves when they arrive at the listening area. Simply stated, sound is nothing more than rapidly changing air pressure. If the air at your ears changes its pressure slightly 30 times each second, you'll "hear" 30 Hz sound. Now for a speaker to produce a 30 time-per-second change in air pressure, it must move its cone back and forth and actually "push" the air in a series of 30 pressure-increasing/decreasing moves. Our point is simply that if speakers are connected out-of-phase and the same note, or sound, is being reproduced by both speakers simultaneously (as is usually the case with bass sound), one speaker will try to compress air by moving its cone outward while the other is trying to *reduce* the air pressure by moving its cone away from you. The result is a standoff. The low note is poorly heard because the increasing pressure from one speaker is cancelled by the decreasing pressure from the other.

The amount of wire you'll need depends, obviously, on where you'll be mounting the speakers. Determine how many feet you'll need and add some to give you a little leeway. I have run short of wire enough times; I don't want anyone else make the same mistake.

Whenever I measure to see how much wire I'll need for a project, I figure it on the safe side. Allow yourself some slack. The wire will have to be out of sight in the finished product and that may require routing it around this and over that. And

Fig. 4-17. Route the speaker wires for the speakers installed in the rear of the van along the gutter at the top of the walls and then feed them through the frame that runs along the edge of the windshield. They then can be connected to the tape deck from under the dash and will be completely hidden.

every turn uses up more wire. So give yourself some breathing room and buy extra. A good place to route the wire for the speakers in the back of the van is in the gutters that run along the tops of the walls (Fig. 4-17). The wires are hidden and easily accessible until the ceiling goes up. The wires can then be routed through the frame of the van and under the dash to where the deck is to be mounted. For the time being, the wires will just hang, but soon, speakers will be connected.

The only wiring you can do for the tape deck at this stage of the game is to run the 12 volt supply wire. Use 14 gauge automotive primary type wire for this purpose. If the deck you'll be installing has a fused power wire, the only thing you need to do is tap twelve volts somewhere. This could be done from the cigarette lighter, fuse block, or the battery itself.

That should complete all the wiring that you need at this time. Everything else relating to the installation of the sound system is taken care of at a later date.

Chapter 5

Wiring

On the surface the wiring step may seem like a big drag, and it will be if you don't approach it with the proper frame of mind. Don't expect to finish the job in minutes. You can't just grab a handful of wire, a soldering gun, and start stringing wire. It takes careful planning to come up with a system that does everything you want it to do. And that's the first step: planning.

Get a pencil and piece of paper, find a place where you can do some brainstorming, and set to work. First, make a list of items you might want to include. Think of any electrical gadgets you think might be handy to have. This is a chance for you to really give free rein to your imagination. Don't feel inhibited. Make the gadget list as long as possible. There's nothing taboo about having lots of knobs and buttons as long as they all serve a useful function. And there are plenty of gadgets available that do that. For instance, something as simple as a map light can be a tremendous aid while on the open road. It's a bit frustrating to not be able to see where you're going—let alone where you've been. A map light is super cheap and extremely simple to install.

Other useful but simple gadgets are light dimmers, a warning light and buzzer to remind you when the headlights are left on, power vent fan, a clock, and automatic headlight dimmers. Of course, there is always the other class of gadgets—B&W or even color television, tape decks with remote control capability, and electric skylights. If you are in the money, you can really give your imagination a free hand. In fact, you could turn your van into a "James Bond" type vehicle. Most of us, unfortunately, can't afford these expensive items. We must be satisfied with the simpler, more realistic ones.

THE POWER SYSTEM

Once you've come up with what you feel is a complete list of electrical items you might want to include in your van's wiring system, it's time to get down to practical matters. Are there any items that will require lots of power? Do any of the items require a 115 volt 60 Hz power source? These are questions that need to be answered before you can proceed with the actual planning of the wiring system.

The Two-Battery System

If there are any appliances or items on your list that draw lots of current, the one battery in your van may not be enough to do all the work. There is only so much power that can be used before you have to start worrying about whether your van is going to start. In order to determine if you need an auxiliary battery you must determine the amount of current that will be drawn by all of the added on electrical items.

Appliances that you add will either have a wattage rating or a current rating. If the appliance is designed to operate from a 12 volt power source and the wattage rating is given, you simply divide the wattage rating by 12 to get the current rating. If the appliance is designed to operate from a 115 volt power source, you will again divide the wattage rating by 12. This will give you the current that must be supplied from a 12 volt source. If the appliance is a 12 volt appliance and the current rating is given, just jot down the current value. If the current rating is given on a 115 volt appliance, you must multiply the rated current by 10.

Next add up the current that is used by all of the appliances. Did you remember to multiply the rated current of all 115 volt appliances by 10? A typically converted van may have a total current requirement of 20 amperes if many appliances are added. Now that you know the maximum current draw, try to determine how many hours you intend to run your appliances while the van is parked (motor off and the

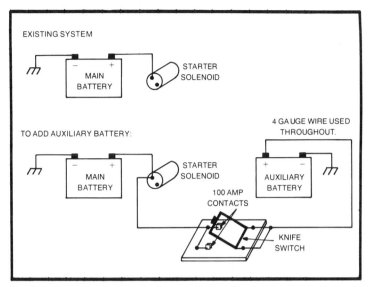

Fig. 5-1. To add a battery to the existing system in your van, all that is needed is a knife switch capable of handling 200 amps and some 4-gauge stranded wire. The connection between the auxiliary battery and main battery should be kept as short as possible to avoid a power loss in the wire. Connect the negative side of the auxiliary battery to the ground bolt on the engine. The main battery can be isolated while camping by moving the knife switch to the off position. To charge the auxiliary battery, close the knife switch. Keep the auxiliary battery fully charged at all times and you'll have a boost available. If, for some reason, the main battery in your van won't start the engine, simply close the knife switch. The auxiliary battery, combined with the main battery, will easily start the engine.

charging system not working). Multiply the calculated current by the number of hours. For example, if your maximum current draw is 18 amperes and you intend to run your appliances for 6 hours, you will need a battery rated at 108 amp-hours.

Most original equipment batteries are rated at 65 amp-hours capacity. A good rule of thumb is that if your electrical requirements are greater than 50 amp-hours, you should add a second battery to your van. The second battery is placed in parallel with the original equipment battery. The original equipment alternator is usually sufficient to charge both batteries.

When the charging system is not operating (van parked with motor off) the second battery should be disconnected from the regular battery. All appliances should be powered by the second battery. Fig. 5-1 shows a simple method to connect two batteries in parallel using a knife switch. When the van is parked the knife switch is opened, isolating both batteries. When driving the van, the knife switch should be closed so that the second battery will be charged.

The second battery is usually mounted in the rear of the van behind a wheelwell. Since the battery emits hydrogen gas while being charged, the battery area must be well ventilated. The battery should be mounted in a plastic battery box. Battery boxes can be purchased at any marine supply house. The battery box will have a lid that covers the battery. Most boxes have provisions for connecting a hose to the lid. The hose should be routed to a hole in the rear area of the van so that the hydrogen gas will be vented to the atmosphere. Don't neglect this venting procedure. All it takes is a spark in a poorly vented battery area to cause an explosion. Play it safe—do it right!

If you don't like to be bothered with the knife switch arrangement for connecting and disconnecting the second battery, you can purchase a dual battery charging system. This is a relay that senses the charging system output. If the charging system is working, the relay contacts close and both batteries are connected in parallel. Stop the van and the relay isolates both batteries automatically. This relay will cost under ten dollars. Follow the wiring instructions supplied with the relay. A similar system is available consisting entirely of solid-state devices. With these, the charge-discharge-isolation procedure is entirely automatic. There are no switches to throw or relays to energize.

The main disadvantage to the two battery system is money. Car batteries are quite expensive these days. But if you have the money to shell out, you can have all your gadgets and not worry about your van not starting. It won't matter if the gadgets draw lots of power. So the first bridge is crossed. But that still leaves one more. Do any of the items on your list require a 115 volt power source?

Inverters

If your answer to the last question is yes, you'll need a power converter, or inverter (Fig. 5-2). It's a device that changes 12 volts DC (your car battery) to 115 volts AC. With the addition of this nifty item, a whole range of useful features is opened to you. You can now run anything from an electric shaver to a vacuum cleaner in your van, depending on the

Fig. 5-2. An inverter changes 12 volts DC to 110 volts AC. The two transistors on the bottom of this unit handle a total of only 40 watts but larger units are available that can handle as much as 1000 watts. The cost of these units is much higher than this one, however.

inverter's power output and the accessories' power requirements.

The amount of power that inverters are capable of supplying is rated in watts. Some inverters handle 40 watts (as does the one shown in Fig. 5-2) while others can supply hundreds. They all work under the same principle. A 40-watt inverter puts out enough power to run a 40-watt bulb. Likewise, a 100-watt inverter puts out enough power to run a 100-watt light bulb. It's that simple. If the 115 volt gadgets you want to include will draw much power, the size of the inverter must be figured accordingly. For instance, suppose you want to install a coffee maker in the back of your van. The coffee maker uses a heating element that draws a lot of power. Just how much power the unit draws is usually stamped somewhere on its case. The inverter will have to handle as much power as the coffee maker needs. That could be as much as 1200 watts. And a 1200 watt inverter is going to be outrageously priced. Actually, it would be far better to invest in a small stove if all you want to do is use a coffee pot. It's really not practical to "convert" electricity at those power levels.

LIGHTING

No van conversion would be complete without an adequate lighting system. Whether you plan to use the van as a camper or a rolling penthouse, effective lighting will greatly increase the pleasure you derive from your finished product. Here again, careful planning is essential. It is important to know exactly where any lights will be mounted and how they will be connected *before* you begin the actual installation process. But first, decide on the type of lighting you are going to use.

You are again faced with two choices—the lighting can be the standard incandescent type or it can be fluorescent. As with the inverter and the dual battery system, disadvantages exist for both types of lighting. Incandescent bulbs draw much more power than fluorescent lamps for a given light output. But fluorescent lights can't be turned on at the flick of a switch. A button must be held down until the bulb "starts" at which time the button is released. If the car battery is low or the inverter puts out very little power, the button may need to be held down as long as 20 seconds. If you want instant light, fluorescent lighting is not the way to go. But if you want to get by with an inverter that puts out little power and is thus inexpensive, and you want lots of light, fluorescent lighting is the *only* way to go. The colors in your van interior will look different under fluorescent lighting than they would under incandescent lighting. They will appear to be more "electric." The overall effect is one of modernness as opposed to the romantic mood that can be created with incandescent lights. You'll get lots of light using fluorescent bulbs and very little power consumption, but you'll pay a price in a way other than monetarily. If you're interested in creating a romantic mood in your van, fluorescent lights just don't cut the cake! Incandescent lights used in conjunction with a dimmer can be made to very closely approximate the same lighting candles would create. Coupled with a high-quality sound system, the effect can be most pleasing. But here too you must pay for your pleasure. The increased power consumption of 115 volt incandescent lights will increase the size requirements of your inverter. If you require only very little light, you could get by with using standard 12 volt automotive type light bulbs instead of using 110 volt lamps.

Placement

The placement of lights may seem an incidental problem, but it can mean the difference between a fair lighting system and a great one. If the lights are carelessly strewn about the interior of the van, everything may work out all right, but then again, it might not. Don't leave it up to chance. And don't decide where they'll go as you install them. You'll be making a big mistake if you do. You'll find yourself running short of wire and compromising the position of your lights. Make the positioning of the lights a separate step from the installation.

Take a piece of paper and a pencil, sit in the back of your van, and decide where you want each light to go. Write it down so you won't have any doubts when it comes time to do the actual installation. If any of the lights are intended to be used while the van is moving, they must be mounted where they won't disturb the driver. In fact, in some states it is illegal to have a light on inside a vehicle in motion. Positioning the lights so they won't disturb the driver will make your van safer, and it takes little extra work.

You may want to position one light toward the front of the van and one light toward the rear. This is what I did in my first conversion job and it worked out quite well. While the van was moving, the front light could be turned off but the rear light could be left on without disturbing the driver. Of course, there is no need to restrict yourself to just two main lights. Put a light wherever you think it would be useful. A lighted storage compartment is a big improvement over one that isn't. A reading light for your passengers can decide whether your conversion will be commented on or not. And we all dig an occasional compliment!

A swivel-type light is a very useful device in a van. It can serve the purpose of several lights. It can be aimed in any direction you want, so it is possible to get by with one light where you would normally need two or more. I mounted a swivel light behind each front seat once. That way either person sitting in front has a light at his disposal. But I put the switch for the passenger side light on the driver side of the van. I wanted to be able to control when the passenger light was turned on. Otherwise, somebody might carelessly turn it on while driving through traffic at night and cause problems. Still, the swivel light is very useful when mounted here. All the person has to do is ask and he gets all the light he needs.

There are several wild things you can do with your ceiling and lighting system if you're willing to invest the time. For instance, a suspended ceiling that has lights behind it would look very nice. When light shines through the hundreds of tiny holes you'll put in the ceiling panels, they look like stars. This is quite an ambitious project and should only be attempted if you have lots of time on your hands. But you'd probably have the wildest lighting system around.

The important thing to remember when planning where lights will be mounted is to try to think of everything now. It will be difficult to try to include an idea at a later stage of the game. The diagram for the wiring will already be planned, the walls will be up, and your mounting possibilities will be greatly reduced. So try to think of everything before you continue with the wiring step.

Switching

It was important to me to be able to have sole control over the swivel lights mounted behind the two seats in my van. It might be important to you. In fact, the problem of controlling the lights you have decided to install is one that must be dealt with. The lights won't just respond to your whims. You have to design your system to be controlled.

Here is another instance where your imagination can work for you. The area of switching can be the most enjoyable step in wiring your van. If your system is designed properly, you can have light at your fingertips regardless of where you are in the van. All it takes is switches and some simple planning.

Once you've decided where the lights are going to be mounted, decide where you'll want the controls. If you are going to include a bed in your van, you'll probably want a switch close by so you won't have to fumble through the darkness trying to find one. If you plan to use the floor as a bed, it might be nice to have a switch mounted very low in the wall so it can be reached while lying down. It wouldn't take much. Toggle switches to control lights are simple and cheap. Wire is reasonably cheap. All you add is time and a little skill.

Figure 5-3 shows how one light can be controlled from two different places. Many homes use this system; it's the famous 3-way switch. The light can be turned on or off from the top of the stairs as well as from the bottom. As you can see, the method is really very simple. It's just a matter of connecting two wires to two switches. The light can now be controlled from two different places. You must, as shown, use *single pole, double throw* toggle switches for this application.

There are many other neat little things you can do with switching. Just use your imagination. With a *rotary* switch you

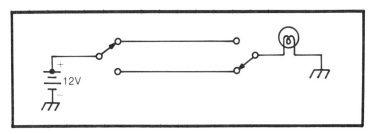

Fig. 5-3. Controlling a light from two places is much simpler than it at first appears. All that is needed is two switches and some wire. The switches needed are single pole, double throw type.

could control all the lights in your van from one location. You could even have any combination of lights on at any given time. Position A on the rotary switch could turn on the front lights and a swivel light while position B, C, or D could control a rear main light and any other lights you want. The same effect could be achieved with a bank of toggle switches. For every light in your van, there would be one toggle switch. The toggle switches could be laid out in one neat row where they are easily accessible. In this way you could have the most complete control over your lighting system that is possible. The finished product would look complicated and people would surely comment on it but it would really be quite simple. Figure 5-4 shows how one switch is connected to a light fixture. The van chassis acts as the ground conductor which connects one end of the lamp to the negative battery terminal, thus "completing" the electrical circuit. A control panel is just numerous switches, connected to lights as the switch in Fig. 5-4 is, and brought together in one place.

Another project might be the addition of several colored lights. They're great for altering the mood inside your van. If it is cold outside, a red lamp will make the inside of the van seem warmer than it really is. There's lots of room for experimentation here.

FUSING

If you're interested in doing a really first-class job on your van, proper fusing is something that should definitely be included on your list of things to do. Like a house, a van wiring system will sometimes malfunction. A light may short out; water may work its way into something it shouldn't, form rust, and the rust could flake off and short a circuit. For these reasons, it is necessary to have an automatic system that will shut off the power if anything goes wrong. Fusing will accomplish this.

Depending on how concerned you are with this step, you can make it super elaborate or just functional. Some companies market fuse boxes and circuit breakers especially designed for vans. They are very similar to the systems being used in many houses these days. Circuit breakers automatically cut the power off if there is any problem in the wiring and can be "reset". A fuse, once it does its job of protection, must be replaced once the electrical fault is found and corrected. The cost of such units vary, but generally it is safe to say they are quite expensive. The same task can be performed in a much cheaper way. All it takes is a visit to a local electronics supply house where you'll find a fuseholder. This is connected in series with the hot wire between the battery and the control panel (or the individual light fixtures if you like) as shown in Fig. 5-5. It's not as sophisticated as the fusebox, but it works as well. If a fuse blows, it must be replaced in this system, while the circuit breaker, as we said, can simply be reset. The cost of this system is substantially lower than the fusebox, to say the least. Fuses should be placed as close to the power source (battery) as possible. Remember, any wire between the fuse and battery terminal is *not* protected.

THE HARDWARE

Once you've decided *where* the parts to your wiring system are to be positioned, the next step is to select them.

The Lights

When in the market for light fixtures, your best friend is your common sense. Don't be swayed by sensational

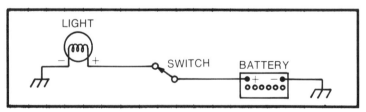

Fig. 5-4. Connecting a light to a power source is surprisingly simple. For a 12 volt light one wire goes to ground. The other goes to the switch. The battery is connected to the remaining contact on the switch.

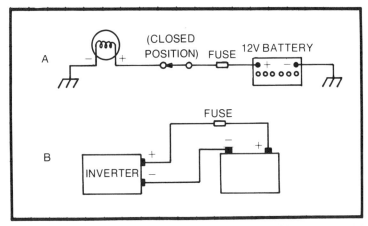

Fig. 5-5. Fusing the lights is a good idea. If a short should occur in any of the fixtures or at one of the connections you've made, the fuse automatically shuts off all power to the lights. This is a safety precaution that you'll probably never have to use but it is better to have that protection just in case something should go wrong.

advertising. When deciding on what light fixtures to buy, select one that is sturdy and simple. Don't assume that they all work equally well. I did that and made a bad buy. I bought two fluorescent lights at a discount store that were on sale. When I got around to installing them, I found why they had been on sale. There's always a reason and often its poor quality. I was so interested in saving money that I forgot to check for quality. Examine the fixture carefully, as I should have done. The case should be tight; there should be no rattles.

Some light fixtures come with a switch built in. There is no need to buy this kind since you will be installing your own switches, but if it costs you no extra, that's fine. It will give you that much added control.

The Switches

The type of switch needed to control lights is known as the single pole, single throw type. The switch makes a connection between two leads of a wire as shown in Fig. 5-4. It is available at virtually any hardware store. I've even seen them sold in grocery stores. In my van I used what are called ''rocker switches'' as pictured in Fig. 5-6. A push on one end turns something on; a push on the opposing end turns it off. But this isn't the only type available. It's just a lever that when moved one way the connection is made; when moved in the opposite

Fig. 5-6a. Rocker switches are an attractive way of switching things. Their installation is no different than a simple toggle switch but they are nicer looking.

direction, the connection is broken (Fig. 5-6). As to the style of switch to get, that is still to be decided.

A third type of switching device is the push switch. One push of the button turns the switched item on; another push turns it off. Of the three switches mentioned, this happens to be

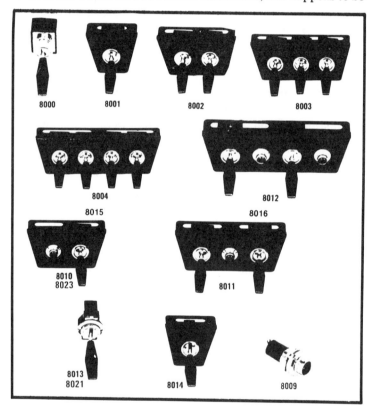

Fig. 5-6b. While a basic toggle switch is not very attractive, manufacturers do try to improve their looks slightly. These are marketed by T & H Works Unlimited and are a significant improvement over the standard bat-handle type so common today.

my favorite. The switch doesn't stick out very far past the surface it is mounted on, so nothing can get caught on it, unlike the toggle switch. The push switch isn't any more difficult to install; in fact, it is easier to install than a rocker switch. A hole is drilled, the switch is positioned, and the collar nut is tightened down. The rocker switch requires a rectangular hole which must often be made with a nibbler.

The Wire

Before you can do any electrical wiring of course, you have to buy the wire. The best type to use is regular automotive primary type wire. You can get it at any auto supply store. It's designed to handle lots of current so there should be no danger of overloading. It's stranded so it is easier to work with than other types. Do not use thin, solid conductor hook-up wire to connect your system. Not only can it handle very little current, because of its small diameters, but it is very difficult to work with. Because the conductor is just one solid piece or strand of metal, it breaks easily when bent. But automotive type wire is stranded and thus bends quite readily—a very important feature since you'll be routing the wire behind this and over that, and bending it considerably.

As to the size of the wire, it should be 14 or 16 gauge (remember, the higher the number the smaller the wire). If it is to be used for something that draws little current, the wire could be as small as 18 gauge, but that should be your limit.

Automotive wire has another point in its favor—and it's a big one: it is color coded. You can get red, blue, green, white, black, yellow, brown, orange. In addition to the basic color of the wire, you can select what color stripe runs along the outside of the insulation. For instance, you might want to use red wire with a yellow stripe for the rear main light and red wire with a green stripe for the front main light. By varying the different combinations of insulations and stripes, the wiring system in your van can be completely color-coded. This can be an extremely advantageous thing to do if there ever comes a time when the system malfunctions. Trying to trace down a problem in your van when all the wire used is the same color can be very difficult. But if everything is color-coded, you'll have no problem locating the problem and affecting the necessary repair. I color-coded the entire wiring system in my personal van by using wire with red insulation for the lights and blue wire for the sound system. Green was reserved for miscellaneous gadgets I had included. I then sub-coded each system using the stripes on the insulation. Blue with a red strip designates the hot wire for the tape deck. Blue with a yellow stripe denotes the front left channel, while blue with a white stripe is the code for the front right channel, and so on. As you can imagine, this system of coding makes troubleshooting the wiring system at a later date very simple. It's important though, to keep an accurate record of what colors lead to what. A list of everything electrical in your van along with the color code for that device is sufficient.

FINAL PLANNING

Let's say you've decided where all the lights will be mounted, where the switches will go, and what gadgets you're going to include. Now it's time to consolidate all that information into one master plan. Make a diagram showing *exactly* how everything in your wiring system is interconnected. This diagram will be your schematic, or map, when you finally begin the actual wiring of your van. If you try to store all this information in your head, the chances of mistake are increased. Keep it on paper so you'll know exactly where you're going.

Start with the lighting system. First, make a rough approximation of the floor of your van on paper. Then show where each light will be mounted. Then, draw lines between those fixtures and the power source you are going to use representing the wires to be connected. On each line make a note of the color code for that wire. Once that is complete, do the same with your electrical conveniences. When finished, you should have a detailed plan showing how each item in your system is connected along with the proper color codes for each. Check the diagram over several times to make sure it is correct. Figure 5-7 shows what your diagram should look like when you are finished.

It's important to make the drawing first and then begin the actual wiring to avoid confusion. It is very easy to get confused when working with more than four wires, and the chance of making a mistake increases. So cover yourself all along the way. On paper first, and you'll know that everything will work when you're through. Okay, enough said!

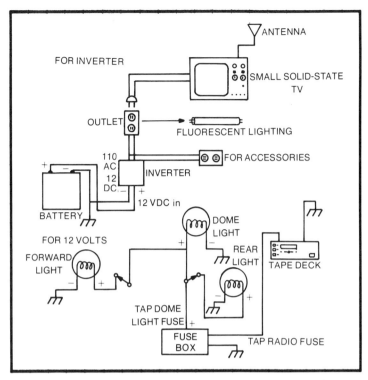

Fig. 5-7. After the wiring diagram is complete you will have a road map to aid you in the following steps. Check the diagram over and over to be certain that you've included all that you want to and to make sure there are no mistakes.

INSTALLATION

The tools needed to wire your van are very common. A soldering gun or iron, solder, a pair of cutters, long-nose pliers, wire strippers, a screwdriver, and some electrical tape should get you started.

Start with the power system. If you are going to use a two-battery system, install that extra battery. Follow your diagram exactly and connect the battery to the existing electrical system. If you're going to use an inverter, mount if first and then connect it to the battery. There will be two leads coming from the inverter (or terminals for two wires); one is designated positive and the other negative. Connect the positive lead to the positive side of the battery. (The positive wire should have an in-line fuse installed as shown in Fig. 5-5b.)

Once the power system is installed, you're ready to start running the wires for the electrical items you are going to include. The easiest way to connect all the lights and gadgets to a power source is to use a control panel. The panel consists of switches for the individual items. Power is connected directly to the control panel, not to the individual fixtures. Figure 5-8 shows how it's done. For a 12-volt control panel, one hot wire is connected to the battery and everything else gets its power from that control panel. This way, there is only one wire that comes from the battery to all the fixtures. The other wire on the fixture is grounded, as is the negative wire of the battery. In effect, you are using the body of the van as one wire. (If an inverter is used, two wires that carry the 145 volts must be connected to each fixture; nothing is grounded. For safety, the body of the van should not be used as a common

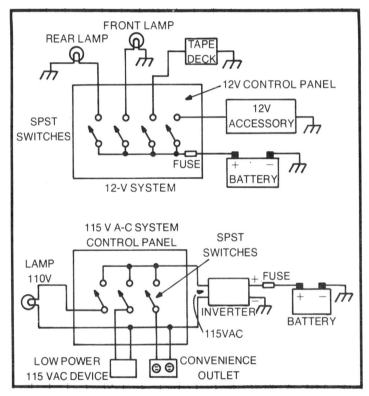

Fig. 5-8. Instead of connecting multiple hot wires to the switches on a control panel, connect only one and tap it for the rest of the switches. This makes for a neater installation and the use of much less wire.

wire, so two wires must be connected between the control panel and the inverter.) The control panel is just a way of consolidating all the hot wires for the various electrical items.

Let the wires hang for the time being. Route them so they are out of the way as much as possible and cut them to the proper length. When the walls go up, they will hide the hanging wires completely, but if you route them carelessly now, they'll be in your way until then. The gutter along the top of the van wall is a very good place to route wires. Keep the routing as simple as possible. Avoid routing the wire through a strange path that is long or consists of lots of turns. The ideal routing would be a direct line from the fixture to the power source or control panel. But this isn't always practical, so a compromise must be struck. Maintain the ideal as much as possible.

All connections should be soldered so they don't work loose and taped to prevent electrical shorts. That's about all there is to the actual task of wiring. The wires are cut to length, routed in the simplest way possible, and left to hang until the walls go up. Once the walls are up and the fixtures and gadgets are installed, your electrical system should be functional. Follow your diagram to stay on the right track.

Chapter 6

The Walls

Originality is what makes the difference between a factory conversion and a do-it-yourself conversion. If you exercise a little originality when installing walls, your van is sure to be even more special than a factory special.

PRELIMINARY INFORMATION

There are several approaches open to design walls. A common design completely covers the walls with carpet, usually the same carpet used to cover the floor as shown in Fig. 6-1. I shy away from this idea for several reasons. One, the amount of dust the carpet will introduce into the air in the van is substantial. Just brushing against the carpet will release thousands of dust particles which eventually either settle on the interior or wind up in your nose; neither is very pleasing. Secondly, carpet is very expensive and it takes many yards to cover the walls. Since high-quality shag carpet has an astronomical price per yard, using it to cover the walls is totally impractical from my point of view. And finally, the carpet on the floor will wear much more quickly than the carpet on the walls. So after a few weeks, the two no longer match.

Paneling

Another common approach is wall paneling. An example is shown in Fig. 6-2. I've seen many vans that used regular

Fig. 6-1. Covering the walls with carpet gives a cave-like look. This feeling is amplified if the carpet on the walls matches the carpet on the floor. This is an expensive way to go so make sure you've looked into cheaper, but no less pleasing alternatives before you plunk down lots of money for carpet.

den-type paneling and, while it looked okay, it was nothing to write home about. I don't care for the den-type paneling because it is to common. You can see it in virtually any office

Fig. 6-2. Paneling the walls with prefinished plywood gives a very contemporary look as well as making the van much less cozy than the previous approach. But paneling is much cheaper and so might be a more desirable way to cover the walls than carpet.

building, church, or school. I personally opted for a more original approach.

Plywood

Covering the walls with plywood instead of prefinished paneling gives you much greater freedom to determine what the walls will look like when completed. The plywood can be covered with practically any flat material. Mirrors, upholstery material, paint, wallpaper, and even sheet plastic have been used.

Walls of the van in Fig. 6-3 were covered with upholstery material, and as you can see, it's a nice change from standard

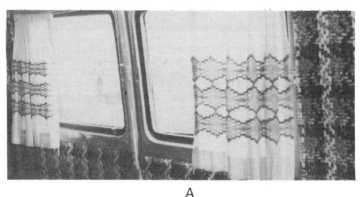

A

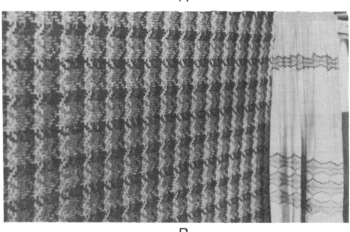

B

Fig. 6-3. Upholstery material is a third alternative for covering the walls. It is less expensive than the previous two approaches and makes for a very nice conversion.

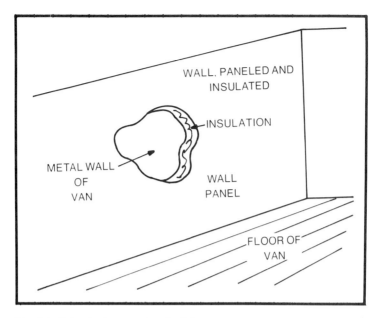

Fig. 6-4. Between the metal wall of the van and the plywood wall panel is three inches of insulation used to cut down on heat loss and drafts, as well as road noise.

paneling. Incidentally, there are countless varieties of upholstery material designs available for you to choose from. In fact, you can probably find a style that suits your interior much better than regular paneling ever would.

Some very distinct advantages go with the decision to use paneling or plywood to cover the walls in your van instead of just dealing with the metal wall itself. You can fully insulate your van walls. The insulation is applied to the metal wall before the paneling goes up (Fig. 6-4). With the increased heat-holding capability of your van, the factory heater will warm a greater portion of the interior. Drafts will be substantially reduced, and your van will not get as hot inside when parked in the sun. Any way you look at it, insulating your van is an intelligent modification.

Another advantage of using paneling to cover walls is a big one—the walls can be used to hold speakers, lights, switches, book racks, you name it. But there is a size restriction. What you want to mount in the walls can not be more than three inches deep. That of course is the depth of the van wall. Three inches is plenty for many types of speakers and virtually any switch you might want to use. There's something really professional looking about a flush-mount installation. The unit is completely out of the way yet still easily accessible. And with space at such a premium in a van, it doesn't make good sense to let the largest percentage of your interior—the walls—do nothing to ease the room crunch.

Doors

Doors are an excellent place to hide a few more speakers, a storage compartment, or even a control panel that matches the walls. With a speaker mounted in either rear door, your van can be used to provide music for outdoor happenings. With the rear doors opened, the speakers are ideally suited for stereo listening as shown in Fig. 6-5. A compartment in a door is a space-saving modification that costs you very little. It's an ideal place to store a flashlight, jumper cables, a few tools (Fig. 6-6).

Partitions

Another design area that is worthy of your consideration is that of partitions. Partitions have become very popular recently because of the versatility of their design. There are two particularly convenient places to install partitions. One is directly behind the two front seats. The partition can form an arched entryway to the back of the van as shown in Fig. 6-7.

Fig. 6-5. With speakers installed in both doors, stereo listening can be enjoyed inside or outside the van. When parked, the rear doors can be opened with the rear speakers ideally positioned for stereo.

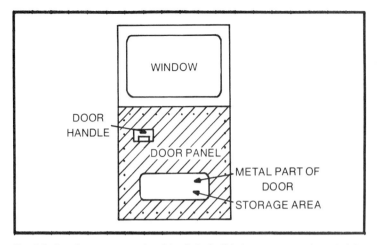

Fig. 6-6. Another space-saving idea is to build storage compartments into the doors. This way space is being used that would otherwise be wasted.

Some people leave the arch open while others prefer a set of doors that can be closed to completely separate front from rear. Aside from affording extra privacy to the rear of a van, the partition is an excellent place to mount speakers and lights. I included such a partition in my van and had a swivel

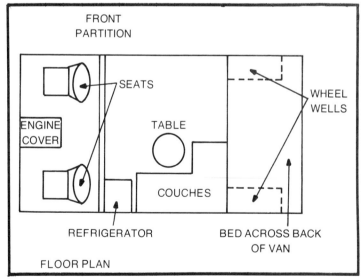

Fig. 6-7. A front partition makes the driver's area feel like another room. Little annoyances are also isolated from the driver, leaving him free to concentrate on his task!

light mounted on either side of the van beside the speakers. Since a speaker was mounted in each front door, the front area of the van was an ideal place to hear quadraphonic music. I included two more speakers facing the rear of the van in the partition so, with the two speakers I added to the rear doors, quadraphonic listening was also possible in the rear of the van. All it took was a partition made of plywood, four speakers, and two swivel lights.

The second partition location in common use is one four or five feet from the rear of the van as shown in Fig. 6-8. Between this partition and the rear doors, many people include a bed or table.

Covering the partitions should be no problem if you've decided to panel the walls of your van. Simply cover them with matching material. Or select a print that is complementary to the walls and add even more variation to the interior of your van. Including a partition in your interior design gives you one more very important edge—it increases the worth of your van. That's a strong incentive to do a really first-class conversion.

You'll probably want to include windows. They're very easy to install, requiring only a saber saw, drill, and screwdriver. But they are rather expensive. The selection available is tremendous, so you shouldn't have a problem finding something that suits your taste. Windows are installed *after* walls are insulated. This is covered in detail in Chapter 9.

Fig. 6-8. A partition farther back than behind the front seats can be installed just as easily. It can be open like this one, or solid.

The time it takes to install walls and door panels in your van will vary, depending on the difficulty of your plans. If there are a lot of items that must be mounted in the walls, naturally it will take you longer to complete the task. And if you decide to first insulate the walls, that will add another hour to the total amount of time needed to complete the task. Allow yourself one full weekend for the entire task. Otherwise you might be pressed for time and be forced to leave the job unfinished. Allotting a weekend for the task will give you plenty of time to deal with any problems that might arise in the installation process.

The actual task of paneling the walls and doors is a relatively simple one. First, anything that might get in your way must be removed. For example, the tire rack. That could be a job because they are usually spot-welded in place. If that's the case in your van, use a drill to break the welds first. Then break the tire rack loose with a hammer. Be careful to avoid damaging the wall in the process.

Second, the van is fully insulated. (If you are going to use fiberglass insulation, work with a section at a time. If the van is fully insulated from the start, you'll have to work around the fiberglass throughout the rest of the installation. We'll deal more with this later.) And third, the paneling is cut to size. All necessary mounting holes are cut in the paneling at this time. Speakers or accessories are mounted in the panels only if they cannot be installed after the panel is in place. Most light fixtures can be mounted after the wall is finished, but speakers and some switches must be installed prior to that point.

The panels are fastened to the metal walls of the van with sheet metal screws; then the walls are covered with material you've selected. I used upholstery material, and the only tools required were a knife, staple gun, and pair of scissors.

The corners of your van will probably give you the most trouble in the paneling step. There's nothing concrete in the corner of a van to fasten a wall panel to. For this reason, you'll have to give this area special attention. It is here that you'll use up that weekend you allowed yourself for the wall installation.

SPECIFICS OF INSULATION

While a house builder might tell you that your choice of insulation is a critical decision and should be made in a reverent manner, the matter is much less critical with respect to a van. A house is a very large area to protect against heat loss—a goal is easily achieved in a van. There are far fewer areas where heat is lost in a van than in a house. Standard insulation available today for homes will be adequate for use in your van if they are installed properly. However, they are not all of equal cost. When faced with a choice, opt for the cheaper variety. The very expensive types of insulation will probably give a sizable increase in heat-holding capability to a house, but in a van, where the situation is much less critical, the extra cost for the good stuff is a waste. There are two types of insulation used commonly in vans today—fiberglass and foam.

Fiberglass

Fiberglass is the cheaper of the two. Usually you can get by with paying half as much for fiberglass as for foam. Unfortunately, you pay for this saving in other ways. Fiberglass insulation is difficult to work with. If you touch it to your bare skin, you soon start to scratch. The itching spreads, or seems to, and before long your whole arm, leg, chest, or whatever, is in desperate need of scratching. Wear protective clothing when handling this type of insulation. Gloves, long pants, and a long sleeve shirt should give adequate protection, but the fiberglass sometimes manages to make you itch in spite of your garb. Fiberglass is hard to cut and hard to stick. But it is cheap and effective. And that's why I use it. I'd rather put up with the inconvenience and save some money.

Foam

This is the insulation used widely in professional conversion shops because of its ease of application. First, while it is significantly more expensive than the fiberglass insulation, the advantages that go along with it may well be worth it to you. First of all, foam won't make you itch. It can be handled without special clothing, and you never need worry about being uncomfortable because of it.

Second, it's easy to cut and apply. A pair of scissors or a utility knife will cut foam beautifully.

Third, the scraps can be put to good use somewhere else in the van. Fiberglass scraps should be thrown away or stored somewhere out of reach

If you can afford it, go with the foam insulation. The ease of handling and application that foam insulation has over fiberglass makes it worth the extra cost. But if you still decide to use fiberglass insulation, don't worry. For all practical purposes, it works every bit as well as the foam. The only problem using it comes during the installation. But once you're past that step, you'll never notice any difference.

SPECIFICS OF PANELING

When selecting paneling for your van, there are two ways to go—prefinished (den-type) and unfinished (plywood). If you've decided to use a prefinished paneling, select something that is strong and durable. That's all. Paneling that is 1/4-in. thick will be strong enough for use in your van. Good paneling this thick is *very* expensive. So you may have to strike a compromise. First choice would be the 1/4-in. thick stock, but 1/8-in. thick stock could be used as well, but your walls will be much less sturdy. Keep that in mind.

If you will be using unfinished paneling, or plywood, certainly use the 1/4-in. thick stock. Compared to the prefinished paneling of the same thickness, the unfinished paneling is very cheap. But using unfinished paneling creates an additional cost—the covering material. If you want to cover the walls of your van with upholstery material, the cost of the material, added to the cost of the 1/4-in. thick plywood could be more than the original 1/4-in. thick prefinished paneling. Also, added work is involved when plywood is used since covering material must be installed. Make your choice accordingly.

When purchasing plywood, be sure to get the indoor type. Plywood is available for inside or outside use. Plywood for use outside is more expensive because it has been treated to resist the elements. Don't spend the extra money for this type. Indoor plywood is significantly cheaper than the outdoor type.

Which ever route you decide to take—prefinished or unfinished—pay attention to what you are being sold. If the corners of the sheets of paneling are smashed, you should get a break in the price. If the sheet of plywood the salesman is trying to sell you has lots of knotholes in it, the price should be lowered.

When selecting a variety of prefinished paneling for your van, *don't skimp!* If you buy plastic-veneered paneling, you may not be happy with the end result. Go for the real thing.

Real wood paneling is significantly more expensive than the plastic-veneered type, but the added cost will be reflected in the nicer interior you'll enjoy.

SPECIFICS OF WALL COVERING

If you've opted for plywood paneling, you are now faced with the problem of finding a suitable covering material.

Mirrors

Using mirrors to cover the walls in your van would be very costly, but you would end up with a very different van. This is one way to make the interior of your van seem much larger than it really is. It will feel like a small apartment. If you can't afford to cover the walls entirely with mirrors, perhaps you could cover just one wall and then cover the opposing wall with another, less expensive material. In fact, leaving one wall unmirrored will produce a very interesting effect. The mirrored wall will have something colorful to reflect. The interior will still look much larger, and you will have gotten by with nearly half the cost.

Mirrors suitable for covering your walls can be puchased in many hardware stores and all building supply stores. The mirrors should be one foot squares, not sheets of glass. The one foot squares will be simpler to apply to the curved wall of your van than a single sheet. Contact cement is ideal for this purpose. Simply apply the cement to both surfaces—the wall and mirror—wait for it to dry, and stick them together. The mirror will be held very tightly against the wall.

Upholstery Material

The selection available in upholstery material is, to say the least, vast. Countless patterns have been developed through the years and most of them are still available. It's just a matter of selecting one you like. I used upholstery material to cover the walls in my personal van and I'm very happy with the end result. I first covered the walls with a layer of 1/4-in. thick foam to give the surface a plushness. Then I stapled the upholstery material in place over the foam. Once cut to size, the upholstery material made a very nice covering for the wall. The cost of the material will vary, depending on its density and quality. You can probably find something to suit your tastes and quality standards for less than $3 per yard.

When selecting a material, there are a few things you should know. One is that stripes or lines can greatly affect the appearance of the interior of your van. If the stripes run vertically on the walls, the van will look shorter than it really is and the ceiling will look higher. If the stripes run horizontally, the van will appear long with a low ceiling.

There are many different textures available in upholstery material. If you select a material that has little texture, you could be missing out on something you like. I used an upholstery material that had a very distinct texture in my van because it added another element to my interior—the sense of touch. Instead of flat, colorless boundaries, the walls were colorful, eyepleasing, and fun to touch as well. Make your selection carefully. It's a decision that you will have to live with for a long time—as long as you own your van. So it shouldn't be made in haste. It's a purely esthetic decision but an important one nonetheless.

To get right down to the common wall coverings, wallpaper and paint are the first things that come to mind. Both are mediums that are seldom used in vans, but the question arises—why not? There are thousands of wallpaper varieties ideally suited to a van's interior. Give consideration to them. It could be a very inexpensive alternative to upholstery material or mirrors. A gallon of paint or a roll of wallpaper is going to cost substantially less than either of the before mentioned alternatives.

There is extra work involved if you use wallpaper or paint. While a smooth wall is not needed for the application of upholstery material or mirrors, it is imperative when using either wallpaper or paint. The wall must be thoroughly sanded before the covering goes on. If it isn't, any abberation on the surface of the wall will show up. And don't expect to get plywood already smooth enough from a building supply house or lumber yard. It just won't happen. So if you decide to go with either wallpaper or paint, you'll be saving yourself lots of money, but you'll also be letting yourself in for much more work. Consider that when making your decision.

As to the actual application of wallpaper, all that is needed is glue. The wallpaper is cut to size, and glued to the wall using regular wallpaper cement which is available at any hardware store.

By now you should have a firm idea of just which type of wall covering you are going to install. You should have decided whether or not you are going to insulate the walls, how you're going to cover them, whether you'll include any partitions, and what you're going to mount in the walls. Next, it's time to compile a list of materials you'll need for the project.

SPECIFICS OF WALL MATERIALS

If you've decided to use fiberglass insulation, you should have no trouble buying the right amount. The fiberglass you'll need is 24-in. wide and will come in a roll of 25 or so feet. All you have to do is determine how many strips of insulation you'll need to cover a wall. Since the insulation is two feet wide, a nine foot wall will require four and one half strips to cover it. To tell how long those stips should be, just measure the height of the ceiling, then multiply the height (in feet) by the number of strips needed to cover the wall and you'll have the number of feet of fiberglass you need for one wall. Double it and that takes care of the other wall. To figure out how much insulation you'll need for the doors, simply estimate it. Since the fiberglass is so cheap, it's no big deal if you have a little extra.

Be sure to get fiberglass insulation with paper backing as you did for the floor. It's easier to handle and holds up better.

If you've decided on foam insulation, the method of calculating how much you'll need is slightly different. Foam is sold by the square yard. Multiply the height of the van's ceiling by the length of the van wall. Get both figures in inches to simplify the operation. Then divide that figure by 1296, which is the number of square inches in a square yard. That should give you the number of square yards needed to cover that wall. Double it to allow for the opposing wall. Then add a square yard for each door to be insulated. And that's it. You have the number of square yards needed to do the job.

How Much Paneling?

Determining the amount of paneling needed to cover the walls is extremely simple. Since you have to buy it in 4 × 8-ft. pieces, you're going to end up with extra paneling no matter how close you figure it. So you might as well just estimate it. If your van walls are nine feet long and your ceiling is four and a half feet high, it'll take approximately one and a third sheets to cover one wall. Add a sheet to cover the doors and allow for any nooks and crannies that will need to be paneled. Three sheets should be just about right for most vans. If you have a very long van or an exceptionally tall one, adjust the number of pieces accordingly. But whatever you're driving, it shouldn't take more than four and a half sheets to cover all the walls and doors.

How Much Covering Material?

Of course the amount of covering material you'll need is the same as the amount of paneling needed. But one thing is different. It is very important for you to select upholstery material wide enough to cover the wall from floor to ceiling with a couple of inches to spare at either end. Upholstery material can't be pieced carelessly the way paneling and insulation can. This is particularly true if there is a pattern on the material. The pattern will have to be maintained when several sections of the material are pieced together. And that's made very difficult if the material isn't wide enough to cover the wall from floor to ceiling.

If you've opted for the mirror idea, it is necessary to determine the number of square feet on the surfaces to be covered since mirrors are purchased in one foot squares. Multiply the height (in feet) by the width (in feet) of the area to be covered and you've got your answer.

Some mirrors come with a peel-off sticky backing. You can save money by buying mirrors without that special backing. A pint of contact cement (all that you're likely to need) is going to cost less than the added cost of mirrors with peel-off sticky backings.

So far your materials list should include:

- Twenty-four inch wide roll insulation or foam.
- About four and one half sheets of paneling material.
- Covering material to cover all the walls and doors.
- Incidental items.

To screw the paneling to the wall you'll need a box of sheet metal screws 1/2-in. long and 1/8-in. thick. A box of staples and some carpet tape will also be necessary. And that's about it for the supplies. Next, you'll need the necessary tools.

SPECIFICS OF TOOLS

Tools needed for a wall installation are basic. The following list should define all you'll need to complete the task.

- Drill with screwdriver attachment
- Flat-bladed screwdriver
- Tape measure
- Sabre saw
- Extension cord
- Pencil
- Carpet tape or spray adhesive
- Straightedge
- Stapler/tacker
- Soldering gun or iron
- Solder

Of course the list of tools you'll need is completely dependent on what you've decided to do with your walls. But this list should cover everything you're likely to need. So let's proceed to the actual installation.

INSTALLATION: INSULATION

The first step in finishing the walls to your van is to insulate. If you are using foam insulation, cut enough strips to cover the wall between the vertical braces. Don't bother insulating the doors at this time. That can be taken care of at a later time when you're ready to mount speakers there. Apply the foam to the wall using spray adhesive or tape that is sticky on both sides (carpet tape). Use only enough to hold the insulation in place until the paneling is up.

If you're using fiberglass insulation, the procedure is slightly different. The fiberglass is cut with scissors to the proper length. (It will already be cut to the proper width—24 inches—the same distance between the vertical braces on your walls.) Just roll off a piece long enough to cover the wall from floor to ceiling between the braces, cut it and apply it. Be sure the fiberglass is applied to the wall with the paper side facing the exterior wall. The paper surface will stick to the wall much more readily and hold more firmly than the fiberglass surface.

The insulation should cover the entire wall from the back of the front seats to the extreme rear of the van. Don't skimp! Make sure the walls are covered with insulation wherever possible. With that done, you're ready to proceed to the actual paneling process.

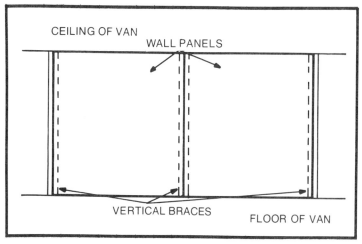

Fig. 6-9. The edges of the wall panels should fall in the center of the wall braces. If a brace is entirely covered by the edge of one panel, the next panel will have nothing to bolt up against.

INSTALLATION: PANELING

So far the back of your van contains walls that are covered with insulation and wires hanging in several places. Once you complete the paneling step, the van should be taking definite shape as a conversion job. The wires will be hidden along with the insulation. If you're using unfinished plywood, the next step will be to cover the walls; but, we'll cross that bridge when we come to it. Now, we're concerned only with getting the paneling up.

Walls

The first step is to select an area that you want to panel first. Pick an easy one so you can get the feel of what you're doing before working the difficult corners or wheel wells. Avoid these two areas at first since they are the most difficult.

Measure the height and width of the area you first want to cover. Work from rib (vertical brace) to rib. Don't have one edge of the panel extending past a rib. It should fall right on it. The panel to go next to this one should also have its edge on a rib (Fig. 6-9). Then, using a pencil and straightedge, mark out an area of the same size on one of the pieces of paneling. To do this the paneling should be lying face down on any flat surface. (If you're using prefinished paneling, take precautions to avoid scratching the surface that is finished. If you're using plywood, don't worry about scratching it because it will be covered at a later time.)

Once the area is marked out, cut along the line carefully with a sabre saw. If you have a couple of sawhorses lying around, put them to use. You'll be doing lots of cutting and it can be awkward doing it all on the ground.

When the panel is cut to size, get the remaining paneling out of your way. Then, check to make sure the piece you just cut fits where it is supposed to. If it doesn't, make any necessary adjustments in its size to make it fit. It's no big deal if it's half an inch too short in some areas. The size isn't that critical. It is important though, that either edge of the panel fall in the center of a rib on the wall.

Now comes the time when you're going to need that list you made of all the mounting holes for accessories. If there is anything to be mounted in the panel you just cut, the mounting holes should be cut at this time. If speakers are to be mounted in this panel, you can usually find a kitchen plate to use as a template. Don't make the mistake of using a plate that is *the same size as the speaker!* It must be slightly smaller so the speaker will have a secure foundation. The plate should ideally be the same diameter as the cone of the speaker, not the housing.

Find a plate that is this size, mark a circle on the panel where the speaker is to be mounted and then cut along the line. Once that's done, place the speaker face down on the panel. Mark the mounting holes with a pencil. Drill out the mounting holes. Then bolt the speaker to the panel.

If you're using prefinished paneling, you'll probably want to install the speaker grille at this time. The same bolts that hold the speaker in place can often be used to hold the grille. If you're using plywood with the plan of eventually covering it, don't mount the speaker grille at this time. You should try to get an airtight seal all the way around the speaker. If you can't by just tightening the mounting bolts, use some silicone sealant or caulking compound and squeeze a bead all the way around the speaker. Avoid overtightening the speaker mounting bolts so as not to warp the housing. The end result will be a very distorted sound.

After the speaker is mounted on the panel, you must be very careful to avoid damaging it. Speakers are very delicate, and a slip of a screwdriver is enough to ruin them. So be very careful!

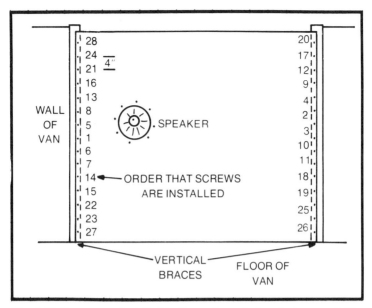

Fig. 6-10. Screws are installed in the wall panels four inches apart. The first two should be centered on either brace as shown.

If the speaker is the only thing to be mounted in this first panel, you're ready to connect the speaker wires. Connect the wires to the speaker observing any color-coding you've done. Make sure that the positive wire goes to the positive terminal of the speaker. The panel is now ready to be fastened to the wall. Put the panel in place and note where the speaker touches the insulation. Cut that insulation away to allow the speaker plenty of room to move freely. Then, using a drill and 1/8-in. drill bit, make one hole in the left edge of the panel about one inch in and centered between the floor and ceiling. The hole should extend into the metal brace. Put a screw here to hold the panel in place while you are fastening it down elsewhere (Fig. 6-10). Now drill a hole directly opposite the first hole you drilled and put a screw there. The panel should now be firmly anchored. Drill holes about four inches above and below either of the first two holes and install screws in each of these four holes. Make sure the panel follows the curve of the van wall closely. It's easy if you hold the panel against the wall firmly with the palm of your hand and drill a hole with the other hand. With the first six screws installed, it should be easy to install the rest. Drop down four inches and install two

123

more screws on the edges of the panel. When finished, there should be screws installed along either edge of the panel four inches apart. That completes the installation of the first panel.

Problem Areas

The next area you select to panel will most likely involve negotiating either a corner or a wheel well. Both are problems that are difficult. But if you proceed slowly and watch what you're doing, you can avoid making any serious mistakes.

Wheel Well. The problem, in dealing with the wheel well, is that, in addition to cutting a panel to the proper size you must also cut out an area of the panel to accommodate the wheel well hump. Since the wheel well is curved, the cutout must also be curved. And that's what makes this operation difficult. The curve cannot be measured exactly. So you'll have to eyeball it. But first, you'll need a few basic measurements.

Measure the height and width of the area to be paneled. Next, cut a panel that will fit that area. Then, hold the panel in place against the wheel well as shown in Fig. 6-11. Trace the outline of the wheel well on the panel. Try to make your mark as accurate as possible. Now remove the panel from the van and cut along the line just scribed. The panel should now fit into place with a little sanding to get it to fit just right.

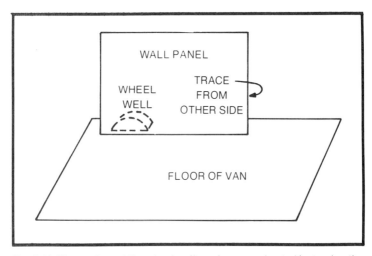

Fig. 6-11. The outline of the wheel well can be approximated by tracing the outline of it onto the panel while it is held in place. Be sure to carefully position the panel before beginning tracing to assure that your cut is correctly placed.

The Corners. Now we come to the most difficult part of paneling the walls (Fig. 6-12). The problem would be simple if there were a vertical brace in each corner. But vans don't have one, so a solution must be found. Like the wheel well problem, the solution is a makeshift one. When dealing with the corner, you are dealing with curves, and since curves cannot be measured with the tools you're using, you must rely on your own judgement and hope you are not too far off.

We will be using the left wall (facing the front of the van) as an example in the next few paragraphs. The last vertical

Fig. 6-12. When finished, the corner of your van should look something like this. Bear your ultimate goal in mind during this step; you want a good-looking van. Don't waste too much time trying to make all your cuts straight. The layers to follow will hide the cuts. If you are using prefinished paneling for the walls, edge molding can be used to hide the cuts.

brace on the wall is approximately three feet from the rear of the van. That brace will provide the only real support for the last panel on that wall. The best way to go about handling the corner problem is to pretend that it doesn't exist. Put up the last panel on the wall and bolt it at only one end. The other end is left free for the time being.

Next, you'll have to cut a piece of paneling to cover the area between the edge of the rear door and the wall. Figure 6-13 shows where you should take your measurements for this panel. Four measurements should be enough to accurately plot the curve of the wall.

Cut a piece of paneling the same length as the height of the van ceiling. Next, using the four measurements you took earlier, mark a line the correct number of inches in from the edge of the panel. For example, if the first measurement you took was at the top of the corner and was four inches, mark a point four inches in from the edge of the paneling in the top corner. If the second measurement was taken 15 inches below the first and was five inches, mark a point five inches in from the edge of the panel and 15 inches down from the last point. This procedure is used for the remaining two measurements.

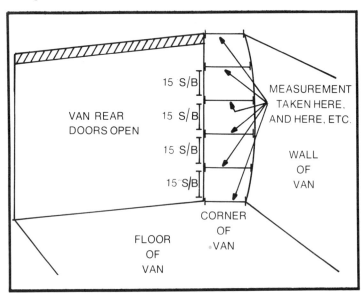

Fig. 6-13. Measure the width of the panel needed at the uppermost part of it. Then measure down fifteen inches and take another reading. Repeat this procedure until you have measurements for the width of the panel spaced at fifteen inch intervals for the entire length of it.

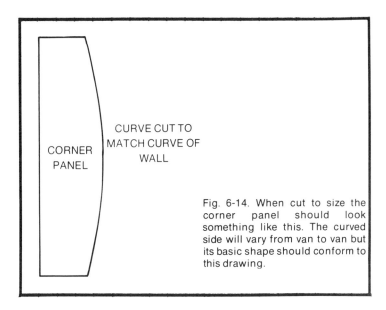

CORNER PANEL

CURVE CUT TO MATCH CURVE OF WALL

Fig. 6-14. When cut to size the corner panel should look something like this. The curved side will vary from van to van but its basic shape should conform to this drawing.

When you're done, you should have four points marked on the panel. Now mark a line that passes through these four points. This should give you a fairly accurate contour of the wall.

Cut out the panel on the line you marked and see if it fits into the corner as it should. If your measurements were reasonably accurate, there will be no problem. You should now have a panel shaped similarly to the one in Fig. 6-14. This panel is now bolted into position to finish the paneling of the corner.

Take a step back and see how it looks. If you are using prefinished paneling, a piece of molding in the corner will hide the actual seam and any small cutting errors you may have made. If you are going to cover the wall with upholstery material, don't worry about how the seam looks. It will be completely hidden. The upholstery material, unlike paneling, doesn't have to be cut to follow the shape of the corner. When the upholstery material is added to the wall, the seam in the corner will be covered.

PANELING THE DOORS

Depending on the make and year of your van, the paneling of the doors will vary in difficulty. If you have an old van, such as a '61 Ford Econoline, paneling the doors is extremely simple. But if your van is of recent vintage and is equipped with a sliding door, the task is slightly more difficult.

Rear Doors

Most vans have two rear doors, so let's start there. Your first step will be to measure the area to be covered. Older vans have a distinct ridge across the door where the panel is designed to stop (Fig. 6-15). But some newer vans aren't like that, as shown in Fig. 6-16. So you'll have to use your judgement as to how high the panel should extend. If there is a

Fig. 6-15. Older vans have ridges on the doors where a panel is supposed to end. This makes the installation of the door panels simpler.

Fig. 6-16. Some new van doors don't have a ridge for the end of the panel so it is up to you to decide how far up the panel should extend. On this door the ridge is present but must be ignored since the entire door must be paneled.

window in the door, you probably don't want to cover it. The panel should extend to the bottom of the window, and no farther. If there is no window, panel the whole thing. Even if you are planning to add a window later, panel it. The hole for the new window can be cut later.

After you've measured the area to be covered on the door, cut a panel to these dimensions. The next step is to mark whatever holes are to be cut in the panel. Let's start with the speakers.

To mount a speaker in your first door, you must make sure it will fit; the door must be thick enough. Many van doors aren't deep enough to accommodate large speakers so make sure yours will fit before you do any cutting.

Once you're sure the speaker will fit exactly where you want it, use the same hole sizing procedure you used to mount speakers in the wall. If the speaker is round, you can probably find the right diameter plate to use as a template. But remember, the diameter of the hole you cut must be **less** than the diameter of the speaker. The plate should be the same diameter as the *cone* of the speaker, not the housing. This is very important, for it provides space for speaker-mounting screws.

If the speaker is not round, use the speaker itself as a template. This procedure is slightly more involved than for the round speaker. First, place the speaker face down on the panel you want it mounted to, and trace the outline of the speaker (mark the mounting holes at this time also). This is *not* the cut line. It is only to help you make the cutting line. You'll need a ruler for the next step. An additional line must be made 3/8-in. inside the first line as shown in Fig. 6-17. Use the ruler to place dots 3/8-inch inside the inner line. This line is the cutting line.

Cut the hole for the speaker and drill out the necessary mounting holes. But don't mount the speaker at this point to avoid damage in future steps. If you are going to include a storage compartment in the rear door, the hole for that must also be cut at this time. Just be careful that the storage compartment doesn't interfere with any moving parts in the door. Also, be sure it's big enough to be functional, not just a hole in the door. First establish the size you want the compartment to be and where you want it located. Then, cut the panel hole and cut a hole in the door. The door hole should be slightly larger than the one in the panel, so the metal door edge is hidden. In some vans, it won't be necessary to cut a hole in the door. Early Ford van doors, for example, had open space.

Once all the accessory holes are cut in the panel, one hole remains. Provisions must be made for the door handle. The problem is non-existent in many applications since most vans don't have handles on the inside of the rear doors. But if your van does, you must accommodate them. For vans with lever-action type door handles the handle is simply removed, a hole drilled in the panel for the handle spindle, and the panel is repositioned.

Some vans, though, will require some special cutting to accommodate the handle. For example, if door handles in your van can't be removed, you'll have to cut an area of the panel away around the handle so that it is accessible after the panel

Fig. 6-17a. The first step in mounting a speaker in the panel is to mark a line around the speaker housing.

Fig. 6-17b. Then points are marked 3/8 inch in from that line. The points should be about three inches apart and go around the entire speaker.

Fig. 6-17c. The points are then connected to form an inner line that is the actual cutting line. **Do not cut on the first line you made**. If you do the speaker will not mount in the panel.

is in place. Figure 6-18 shows a very typical and logical way of dealing with such a handle. Incidentally, the paneling procedure is the same for side doors since they are functionally identical to most rear doors.

Sliding Doors

While paneling a sliding door may seem more difficult than paneling rear or side doors, it really isn't. It's just different. For one thing, most sliding doors will have provision for two windows. If your door has windows, the paneling step is simplified, and the amount of paneling needed is considerably reduced. But if your van sliding door does not have windows, you'll want to panel the entire door at this time. You can always add windows at a later time if you wish.

Once again, the first step is to measure the area to be covered. Then, a panel is cut to these dimensions. An area will probably be cut out for the handle on the door, unless it is the removable type which can then be drilled as discussed previously. If there is to be anything mounted in the door, holes for these accessory items should be cut at this time.

At the top of the sliding door you'll find a bracket to secure the door to the rail. This bracket will have to be removed temporarily when the panel is being installed. But for now, you can work around it. Just get the proper dimensions and cut a panel to size. Cut the mounting holes and then set the panel aside. You are finished with it for now.

Fig. 6-18. If the handles on your doors are not removable, this is one way to handle the situation. Just cut a hole in the panel so the handle can be accessed through it.

Building a Partition

There are many different design techniques open to you in the construction of a partition. It's just a matter of selecting the one that best suits your interior plans. The best type of partition, in my opinion, is one that allows tape decks, control panels, and lights to be installed. It is considerably more elaborate than the most basic partition—the single sheet of plywood. The materials needed are:

- One and a half sheets of 1/4-in. thick plywood
- Two 8 ft. 2 × 4s

The following tools are considered essential:

- Sabre or Skilsaw
- Drill with 1/8-in. drill bit
- Tape measure
- Carpenter's square
- Flatblade screwdriver

First, a 2 × 4 is cut so that it fits snugly between the walls of the van, parallel to the rear doors and the desired distance away from them. This 2 × 4 will serve as the foundation of the partition. Using screws long enough to go through the 2 × 4, flooring material, and metal floor of the van, install the 2 × 4 parallel to the rear doors along the entire width of the floor. If the partition is to have a bed behind it, make sure you install the 2 × 4 far enough away from the rear doors to allow the bed to be installed later. Most beds installed in this manner are around four feet wide so if you bolt the 2 × 4 four feet from the rear doors, there should be adequate room left for the installation of the bed at a later time.

The next step is to install a similar 2 × 4 along the width of the ceiling directly above the one on the floor. Since the ceiling in your van is curved and 2 × 4s are not known for their flexibility, it will be necessary to install the top brace in two sections. First, cut a 2 × 4 to the proper length. Then cut it in half, making two pieces of equal length. Install these two pieces just as you did those across the floor. Cutting the 2 × 4 in half will allow you to make it conform to the curve of the ceiling. It isn't necessary that the 2 × 4 conform exactly to the curve; it must, however, be firmly anchored, and it will serve as the top brace for the partition.

Now two braces must be installed on the walls between the top and bottom brace as shown in Fig. 6-19. Cut a length of 2 × 4 to a size that will allow it to fit between one end of the bottom brace and the corresponding end of the top brace. Then screw it to the wall. If possible, anchor this wood brace in one of the metal braces that runs perpendicular to the floor in the wall. This makes for a much more solid installation. If this isn't possible, however, don't worry. A pretty solid installation can be made nonetheless.

There should now be braces installed across the floor, across the ceiling, and on either wall between the floor and ceiling braces. The next step is to cut the plywood sheets to a size that will allow them to be bolted against either side of the braces. A space between the two sheets will be the same as the width of the 2 × 4s. This space will make it possible for you to install whatever you like in the partition. For instance, you

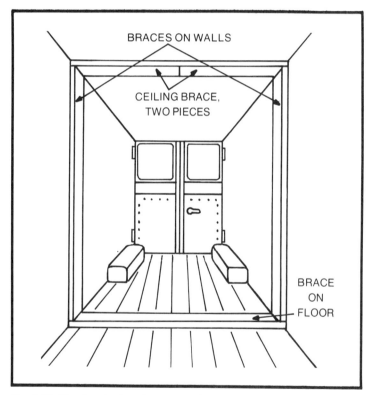

Fig. 6-19. The two by four braces are installed on the walls between the ceiling and floor braces.

might want an extra set of light control switches in the partition that are easily accessible from the bed.

To cut the sheets of partition plywood to size, proceed as follows. Measure the width of the floor and the width of the ceiling where the partition is to be built. Take several measurements at selected levels on the wall. For instance, you might measure the distance between the two walls two feet down from the ceiling and again at a point four feet down. These measurements will make it possible for you to plot the curve of the walls and, thus, cut the sheet of plywood to fit.

Use the same procedure to plot the curve of the ceiling. First, measure the distance between the ceiling and the floor against one wall of the van. Then do the same on the opposite side. Now measure the distance between the floor and the ceiling at several points between the two walls. Three measurements should be enough to accurately plot the curve of the ceiling. With this list of measurements, you can plot the size of the panels.

Lay one sheet of plywood on a flat surface. The first measurement you'll use is that of the distance between the floor and the ceiling. Take the longest measurement (the one taken from the center of the ceiling to the floor) and mark a line on the sheet that many inches from one end of the plywood. This gives you the greatest length of the panel needed. Now take the greatest width of the panel needed (the measurement taken from the center of one wall to the center of the other) and mark a line that many inches from one side of the sheet. These two lines depict the outermost dimensions of the panel. All the other measurements taken are used to plot the curve of the walls and ceiling.

Start at the bottom of the sheet. If you took a measurement between the walls at a distance of two feet from the floor, measure up from the bottom of the sheet a distance of two feet and make two marks corresponding to the width of the panel at that point. For instance, the distance between one wall and the other at a point two feet from the floor in your van might be something in the vicinity of 68 inches. If that were the case, you would measure up two feet from the bottom of the panel, mark a point at that level—34 inches from the center of the panel—and then measure 68 inches across the panel and make a similar mark. This gives you the width needed for the panel at that level. (It may help to mark a vertical line on the panel depicting the exact middle.) This procedure is followed until all the measurements taken have been used. The next step is a simple one. Connect the dots along one side of the sheet in a smooth curve, and do likewise on the other edge. This final line is the actual cutting mark and should be an accurate representation of the curve of the wall in your van.

Ceiling. Plotting the curve of the ceiling is done in a manner similar to that of plotting curves of the walls. First, using the measurement taken from floor to ceiling next to the wall, measure that many inches up from the bottom of the panel and mark a point. Next, do the same with the measurement taken between the floor and the ceiling against the other wall. You should now have three marks—one for the left edge of the panel, one for the right edge, and one for the middle. But three marks are not enough to accurately plot a curve so the other measurements taken from the floor to the ceiling must be used. For instance, let's assume that you measured the distance between the floor and the ceiling at a distance of three feet from one wall. Measure three feet in from that side of the panel and the correct number of inches up from the bottom of the panel and mark a point. Repeat this procedure until you have used all the measurements taken. The rest is simple. Connect these points you marked along the top of the panel to arrive at the proper curve of the ceiling. This is the actual line you will cut on.

With the curve of the ceiling and both walls plotted, you are ready to cut the panel to size. When that's done the panel can be used as a template for cutting the second panel needed. Now you're ready to cut an area out for the doorway to the area behind the partition.

Doorway. First, decide on the shape and size of the doorway. The simplest doorway is a basic rectangular entrance. Decide on the width and the height of the doorway and make a note of the figures. Now you're ready to cut an area of the panel out to correspond to these dimensions. The doorway can be anywhere on the partition that you like. The most common placement is centered between the walls of the van and extending to the floor. But it could be off to one side if you like, or even off the floor entirely (a climb-through portal!).

After you cut out the panel that is to be the entranceway to the area behind the partition, install the panels. Actual installation is very simple; the hardest part is getting them in the van. But once you've done that, just position them and secure them to the braces with wood screws. (Just be sure to route wires that go between the panels at this time; soon this area will be inaccessible.) If you've decided on a doorway that is off to one side of the panel, make sure the areas cut out of the panels for the entranceway correspond to each other in the final installation! It's not impossible to install the pieces backwards. Of course, if the entranceway is to be in the center of the panels, there is no problem since the two panel cutouts are in identical locations.

With the panels installed, your handywork should now look like a partition. It is now necessary to install border braces along the perimeter of the entranceway as illustrated in Fig. 6-20. If the area is rectangular, this is very simple. Just measure the length of one of the sides of the entranceway and cut a 2 × 4 to that length. Position it between the two panels along the edge of the doorway and install screws through either panel extending into the 2 × 4. Repeat this procedure

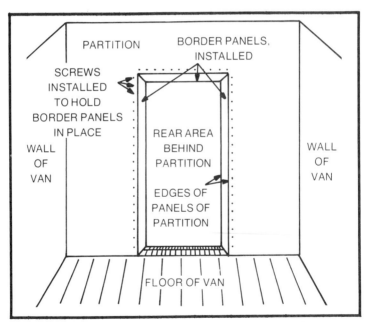

Fig. 6-20. Once the doorway to the area behind the partition has been cut out, the next step is to install border panels around the perimeter of the door opening. Screws are installed from both sides of the partition to hold the border panels in place.

for all the sides of the doorway. That completes the basic construction of the partition.

With the walls paneled, the partition built, and the panels for the doors cut to size and ready to go on, you're ready for the next step. However, the next step varies, depending on whether you are using prefinished or unfinished paneling. If you are using prefinished paneling, all that remains is to add moulding where needed, mount the fixtures and speakers, connect any loose wires, and screw the door panels in place. But if you are using unfinished paneling, the next step is to cover the walls and doors.

INSTALLATION: PANEL COVERING

Naturally, this step varies, depending on what you are going to use to cover your walls.

Upholstery Material

This is by far the easiest step in the installation of the walls. The only tools you'll need are:

- Staple gun
- Tape measure
- Scissors
- Pencil

Before you apply the upholstery material, you might want to cover the walls with a layer of foam. I did this in my van to make the walls more plush. I used 1/4-in. thick foam and just stapled it over the entire wall. The whole job took half an hour.

Try to apply the upholstery material in as large a piece as possible. Don't use lots of small pieces. Larger pieces look much better. First, cut the upholstery material to size. Work on one wall at a time. When sizing the material, give yourself about three inches of breathing room all the way around. For example, if the width of the wall is four feet, cut the upholstery material to a width of four feet, six inches. This will give you plenty of leeway for any mistakes you might make.

In most cases the upholstery material can serve as a grille cover for speakers in the wall. But sometimes this is not wise. If the upholstery material you are using is very heavy, too much sound will be blocked. But if you are using a thin upholstery material, just pretend that the speaker isn't there when covering the wall. This will create an interesting effect when your sound system is in operation. The sound will come from the wall but the actual speaker location will be masked. If the upholstery material you are using is too thick to serve as a grill cover for the speakers, your only alternative is to cover it later with a speaker grille.

When stapling the material to the wall, start at the top and work down. Smooth out any wrinkles as you go. If there is a pattern on the material you are using, try to keep it undistorted. Straight lines on the material should look straight after it is on the wall. Use lots of staples during this step. The material should be held against the wall tightly everywhere.

If it becomes necessary to piece the material together, fold over the edge of one piece and *then* staple it to the wall. This will make a much nicer seam.

Once you've covered the walls, take a screwdriver and tuck in the edge of the material under the wall panel wherever possible. This gives a professional look to your work.

Covering Doors

Spread out your upholstery material face down on a flat surface. Place a door panel face down over the material. Using the panel as a template, cut a piece of material three inches larger than the panel all the way around. Then, fold this excess over the edge of the panel and staple it down. Do this around the entire perimeter.

Fig. 6-21. Once the door panel has been cut to size, padded and covered, it is ready to go on the door. Install a screw at the top of the panel centered to hold it in place through the rest of the installation.

139

If there is a hole cut for a storage compartment in this panel, cut away the material covering this area. Don't cut away the material covering the speaker hole unless the material, as we previously mentioned, is too heavy. If you drilled a hole for the door handle, poke a hole through the material for the handle spindle.

Next, mount those accessories in the door that you cut holes for. Mount the speaker last to prevent damage. Then, connect any necessary wires to the panel (speaker wires, lights, etc.). The panel is now ready to be screwed to the door.

First, drill a hole in the center top of the door panel and center top of the door. Do this by holding the panel in place on the door and drilling the hole through both the panel and the door simultaneously. Put a screw here. This is to hold the panel in place while it is fastened in other places. Drill holes, spaced about five inches apart, along the entire perimeter of the door panel. Use as many screws as it takes to hold the panel tightly against the door as seen in Fig. 6-21, and that's it for the door. Cover and install any other door panels in the same way.

Are You Using Mirrors?

If you are going to cover the entire inside of the van with mirrors, you'll need a glass cutter. Also, you'll need a tape measure, marker, and some contact cement.

Covering the entire walls with mirrors is going to be very difficult since it isn't easy to get a clean cut with a glass cutter. I suggest you cover only part of the walls. You'll still get a nice effect with the mirrors but you'll avoid the hassle of cutting glass. Cover the rest of the wall with carpet, upholstery material, or whatever.

To use mirrors as a wall covering, first mark out the area that you want to cover. Size it so that it can be covered with whole mirror squares. For instance, make it four feet wide instead of 4 1/2 feet. Remember, mirrors come in one foot square pieces.

Your walls should be complete except for the addition of molding where needed. Many types of molding are available, some are specifically designed for use in vans. One such door panel edge molding is made of plastic. It gives the panel a finished appearance in addition to covering any rough cuts you may have made (Fig. 6-22). You may have trouble

Fig. 6-22. Edge molding can be used to hide the ugly cut around the perimeter of the door panel. This is a finishing touch that would be easy to forget but don't do it. Paying attention to little details like this will make your conversion look better.

finding it since it is used pretty exclusively by professional conversion shops. But if there is a pro conversion shop in your town, they are sure to carry it. Conversion stores can be found in ost large cities.

Once you've insulated, paneled, and covered the walls, you're through with this phase of the conversion. Clean up your mess and get ready for the next phase: *Dealing with the ceiling.*

Chapter 7

The Ceiling

The addition of a ceiling to your van interior will take anywhere from four hours to a weekend, depending on the degree of difficulty of your plans. The areas of primary concern when dealing with the addition of the ceiling are:

- Placement and type of lights
- The selection and positioning of sunroofs
- The actual covering material

LIGHTS

The selection of light fixtures to go in your ceiling is a task that should not be difficult. The market is flooded with fixtures of all shapes, sizes, and prices so the chances of finding what you want are great. A popular type of light fixture for the ceiling is the flush-mount unit. Designed to be installed after the actual ceiling is up, it can be added at any time. Two wires are all that is necessary to make the light functional. It's popularity is probably due to the extreme ease of installation and relative good looks. Flush-mount light fixtures are available for the systems using 115-volt inverters as well as the standard 12-volt system. If you're into ease of maintenance, opt for the 12-volt units. The bulbs are cheaper and commonly available at most service stations. The lights designed to be operated on 115-volt sources are no more effective than the fixtures made for 12-volt systems and for low wattage 115-volt

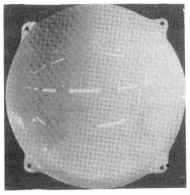

Fig. 7-1. For a contemporary look in lighting, a round light is available from Leisure & Recreational Products in Lake Geneva, Wisconsin.

lamps (those you must use with a power-stingy connector) are a lot less efficient. However, if you can't find what you want in a fixture designed for 12-volt use, there are fixtures to choose from that use the 115-volt source. In fact, many fixtures designed for use in homes can be adapted to fit into the design scheme of a van interior. Usually the modifications necessary are very slight.

Since many people don't care for the flush-mount design, manufacturers have made other designs available. Some people prefer the round look (Fig. 7-1) while still others prefer gimmick lights (Fig. 7-2). These are ones that are designed with some particular style in mind. The one shown is modeled after the rustic style. They are usually made of fake wood.

Fig. 7-2. If the theme for your van is "rustic" this type of fixture should be ideal. It's designed to be installed on the wall but can be mounted just about anywhere. Available from Van Mail, it operates from 12 volts DC so no inverter is necessary.

If you select the efficient fluorescent lighting system, your choice of fixtures is much more limited. Because of the shape of the fluorescent bulb, the shape of the fixture is restricted. The most common type of fluorescent light fixture is a long one designed to be bolted to the ceiling (Fig. 7-3). The long slim design is the most common because it's frequently the only design readily available. But other designs are being marketed. It's only a matter of finding them. Some fluorescent lighting fixtures are designed to accommodate a circular bulb. You've probably seen such a fixture in a kitchen. While these are less popular than the slim units, they are more easily worked into many interior design schemes.

The installation of the light fixtures is extremely simple. It usually involves only two mounting screws and two electrical connections. But if the lights in your ceiling are to be flush-mounted the installation process is made slightly more difficult. Now a hole must be cut in the ceiling panel to accommodate the fixture. A "designer" ring usually goes up around the fixture to hide the actual cut in the ceiling panel. The electrical connections for a flush-mount fixture are the same as those for a standard fixture. There are usually just two wires to connect.

Placement

The placement of ceiling lights should not be rushed. Make your decisions carefully. They'll be permanent in a few days. A misplaced light can not only be a frequent annoyance, it can be a safety hazard.

A standard format used in vans places a main light close to the rear of the van and a similar unit toward the front of the

Fig. 7-3. Fluorescent lights put out more light and consume less energy than standard incandescent lights. If you will be using only one battery in your van, they would be the safest way to solve the lighting problem. Since the drain on the battery is so low, they can be used longer without seriously impairing the battery's ability to start the engine.

van. This way the user has basic, independent lighting control of the front and rear. Auxiliary lights in addition to the two main lights are usually positioned wherever they are most functional.

The underlying rule when positioning lights in your van is make it functional. Position the fixtures so that they can be used in more than one way. For instance, a simple swivel light positioned in the center of the ceiling can serve a variety of functions as opposed to one that is mounted in a corner. Not only can it be used by the people in the back of the van, but it can be positioned to provide added illumination in the front area of the van when needed.

It is also important to give consideration to passenger comfort when positioning the lights. Lights that are mounted toward the rear of the van could irritate passengers when they are aimed toward the front. To aid even more in preventing the misdirection of lights, you might consider installing a master switch near the driver's seat where all the lights in the van can be turned off at any time. This gives the driver ultimate control over the lighting. And if you're really ambitious, you might want to install several switches near the driver's seat to give him control over all the lights independently. Don't make this the only place where the lights can be operated though. That will just make for a very inconvenient system. Each fixture should have a switch somewhere in the rear of the van where it is easily reached. But *ultimate* control over the lighting can be given to the driver with the addition of a simple switch.

SUNROOFS

Including a sunroof in the ceiling of your van is a wise move. It provides very valuable ventilation for the interior of the van as well as a port to view the real world as it flies by.

Types

Depending on how elaborate the sunroof in your van is going to be, the cost varies widely. You could pay as little as fifty dollars for a basic unit that doesn't open. Or you could spend several hundred dollars and get a sunroof that opens and closes electrically. The most common type is smoked Plexiglass that can be opened from inside the van (Fig. 6-4). The price of these units is considerably less than the electric

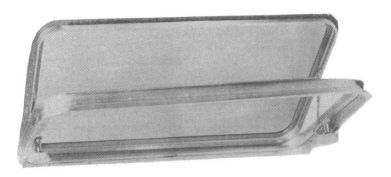

Fig. 7-4. The most popular type of sunroof is of this design—slightly tinted and openable from inside the van. This unit, marketed by T & H Works Unlimited, is as simple to install as a van window.

type. However, I recommend that you select a sunroof that can be opened. Installing one that is simply a window is a waste of time. While looking outside at the sky may be a neat thing to do, ventilating the van is much more important. As I've said, vans can develop very high temperatures inside when parked in the open sun. An inside temperature of 140 degrees is not unheard of. That's enough to damage vinyl if the temperature is maintained for any sizable length of time. But the addition of a sunroof allows an escape route for heat. With a sunroof, you can safely leave your van in the hot sun for hours without damaging the interior. Leaving windows down makes your van vulnerable to thieves. But a sunroof can be positioned to prevent the entrance of intruders when left open.

Sunroofs vary widely in shape and size—some square, some round. But the most common type is rectangular. They are usually about two and a half feet long and a foot and a half wide. Naturally the cost of sunroofs varies with size. As size increases, cost increases. A large sunroof provides a greater degree of ventilation and visibility of the outside world.

In many applications, the size of the sunroof is predetermined by the specific restrictions in a particular conversion. The roofs in some vans are not capable of accepting a sunroof that is any wider than two feet. Others, mostly the later models, are *designed* to accept a sunroof of any size. Normally, it is on the older vans that a problem arises in the actual size of the sunroof. With a little modification, I was able to add a sunroof three feet long and a foot and a half wide. This was the largest that could be

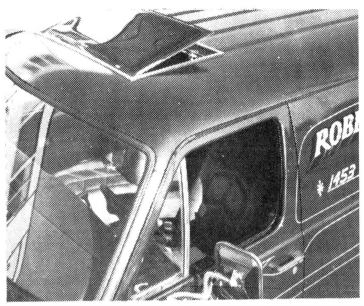

Fig. 7-5. The bubble-shaped sunroof is also very popular but has no advantage over the flat type. In fact, since a bubble-shaped sunroof can be seen more easily from outside the van, it spells trouble for the would-be thief who is looking for an easy route to the inside. The flat type is visible only from above the van.

installed without very extensive modification. While I would have preferred a larger one, this size provides more than adequate ventilation and visibility at a relatively low price.

Sunroofs are most commonly made of plexiglass with metal frames. The plastic part can be smoked or clear, flat or bubble-shaped (Fig. 7-5). A smoked sunroof is preferable for the simple reason that the sun is filtered. Plenty of light still makes it's way through, but the brunt of the bright sun is kept out. A clear sunroof lets the sun, in all its blazing glory, pour through. If the sun happens to be directly overhead, the bright light can be annoying. For this reason, I recommend you go for the smoked sunroof.

Placement

Like the selection of a specific size of sunroof, the mounting location is an area that may not be a matter of choice since only a newer van is specifically designed to accept a sunroof. Most people mount the sunroof directly over the front seats to enjoy it while driving. The ventilation it provides helps considerably on hot days. But, like lots of people, you may find yourself wanting a sunroof in the rear of the van too. Personally, I installed a smaller one midway between the rear of my van and the front. Its primary function was to allow star-gazing from inside the van, but it also served to increase ventilation. So, remember, ventilation and visibility are the two things to consider when mounting the sunroof. The rest is personal preference.

COVERING MATERIAL

The ceilings in most converted vans consist of 1/4-inch plywood sheeting. But how that plywood is covered is an area that allows lots of room for creative expressions. Many people solve the problem of selecting a covering material by using prefinished paneling. While this is an area of pure subjectivity, I recommend that you not use prefinished paneling for the ceiling. Since it is so common, it will probably look old hat. Instead, explore the many different types of covering material available and select something that enhances the interior of your van. Using prefinished paneling is simpler but it doesn't look as good or as original as some other covering materials.

Since the ceiling in your van is slightly curved, the material you use to cover it must be flexible enough to adapt to the curve of the ceiling. Other than that, the list of possible covering materials is unrestricted. If you're interested in an easy route, consider using something like carpet or upholstery material. Both are easy to work with, and they can be applied to the ceiling with either staples or glue. For the amount of time involved in applying either of these two types of covering materials, the finished product looks very good.

If you're interested in going a more elaborate route, you might once again consider using mirrors on the ceiling. Mirrors are not very flexible, they are heavy, and they break easily. These things make the task difficult to say the least. But the finished product is well worth the effort.

Insulating the Ceiling

Ceiling insulation will help the van hold heat in winter and keep the van from getting super hot while parked in summer heat. It doesn't cost much to insulate the ceiling and the advantages you'll get from doing it make it well worth the effort. All that needs to be done is cut the insulation to size and stick it to the ceiling. Use regular fiberglass insulation one inch thick, the same that should be used under the floor. Fiberglass insulation is inexpensive and very effective.

Thus far, your list of materials should look something like this:

- Two sheets of plywood or prefinished paneling 4′ × 8′.
- Sufficient material to cover the entire ceiling.
- Insulation to cover the entire ceiling.

Tools

The tools you'll need for the installation of the ceiling are ones that have been used in many of the steps in this book.

- Electric drill with screwdriver tip and 1/8-in. drill bit.
- Sabre saw.
- Tape measure.
- Flat-bladed screwdriver.
- Extension cord.
- Utility knife or scissors.
- Marker.
- Staple gun.

INSTALLATION

Your first installation step is to remove everything from the ceiling in your way. For instance, if your van has factory dome lights, take them out. The lights you add later will replace them.

Select an area of the ceiling that won't be difficult to insulate and panel. Do that area first so you can get a feel for the procedure. The easiest place to start in most vans is somewhere in the middle of the ceiling. Avoid either end of the ceiling for now because these areas are slightly more difficult. There are between four and six braces running across your ceiling, depending on the make and year of the van. Insulate and panel from brace to brace. Don't try to make the plywood or paneling cover more than two braces. Work with two braces at a time. To cover three would mean the panel would have to be considerably larger, making it much harder to work with.

Measure the distance between the center of one brace and the center of the next one (Fig. 7-6). That gives you the width of the panel needed. Next, the width of the ceiling itself must

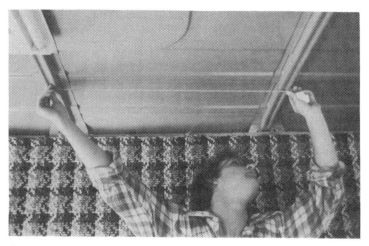

Fig. 7-6. To determine the width of the ceiling panel needed, measure from the center of one brace to the center of the next.

be measured to give you the length of the panel. When you have these figures, cut a panel to this size. Be sure to cut the panel long enough to more than cover the entire width of the ceiling. In fact, it wouldn't hurt to leave an inch to spare on either end.

Once you have the panel cut to size, set it aside for the time being. Your next step is to insulate that portion of the ceiling you will panel first.

Using fiberglass insulation in the standard width of 24 inches and one inch thick, cut a strip to fit lengthwise between the two braces (Fig. 7-7). In effect, cut it to the same size as the length of the panel. Since the insulation is only two feet wide, you'll probably have to cut an odd-shaped piece to fill the gap the first piece will leave.

Attach the insulation with the paper side toward you (Fig. 7-7) using contact cement or carpet tape. Spray contact cement works great for this also. But it's hard to find. In most cases the contact cement will work better than carpet tape. Either way, use just enough adhesive to hold the insulation in place—no more. It doesn't have to be a really strong bond. As long as the insulation stays stuck to the ceiling long enough for you to get the panel in place, there's no problem.

Once the insulation is up, it's time to cut holes in the panel that are needed. If there are to be any fixtures flush-mounted in this panel, their mounting holes must be cut at this time. If

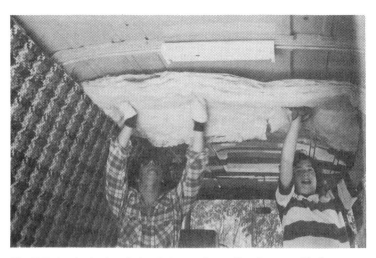

Fig. 7-7. Apply the insulation between the ceiling braces with the paper side away from you. This is going to make the task unenjoyable but it is necessary because the paper must be stuck to the metal ceiling of the van. The fiberglass side cannot be glued to the ceiling.

the fixtures simply screw to the panel, the only hole necessary is one to allow the wires to be connected to the fixture (Fig. 7-8).

With the mounting holes cut and the insulation up, it's time to screw the panel in place. This job will go much easier if you have someone to help you. It can be done with one person but it is much more difficult. Have your friend hold the panel in place. Pull any wires for lights through the mounting holes

Fig. 7-8. Cut the mounting holes for any fixtures before the panel is installed on the ceiling.

(Fig. 7-9). Using a drill with an 1/8-in. drill bit, drill two holes in the general vicinity of numbers 1 and 2 in Fig. 7-10. Install screws in these holes. The panel should now be secure enough to allow you to drill the rest of the holes with no help. Five inches to either side of the first screw, drill another hole (Fig. 7-10). Install screws in each of these four holes. Make sure the panel is held tight against the brace when the screws are torqued down. There should now be three screws installed in either brace. Now drill holes five inches apart along the entire length of either brace. Install screws in these holes and tighten them until the panel is held tight against the brace. And that's it. The panel is installed. This procedure can be repeated for every panel where there are no special problems to contend with.

When you're ready to install the panel closest to the rear of the van the installation procedure must be varied somewhat. One end of the panel is screwed to a brace the same way the other panels were. But the other end of that panel must be dealt with in another manner. Since there is no brace to screw this end of the panel to, it is necessary to screw it directly to the body of the van as shown in Fig. 7-11. The panel must be cut slightly wider than usual so the rear edge can be screwed to the wall. Have a friend hold the panel in place. Then, pull any wires through the proper mounting holes. The two screws that hold the panel in place in the beginning are now installed the

Fig. 7-9. The wires for the light fixture must be pulled through the mounting hole before the panel is permanently anchored to the ceiling. A friend is needed to hold the panel in place while the screws are installed.

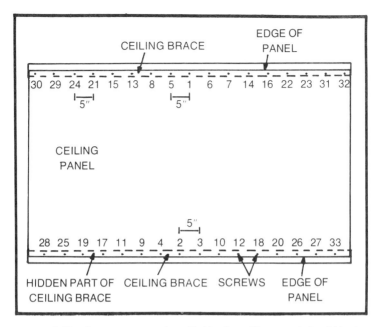

Fig. 7-10. The first two screws installed in the ceiling panel should be installed centered on either brace. Next screws are installed five inches to either side of these two screws. This procedure is followed until screws are installed five inches apart along the entire length of both braces.

Fig. 7-11. The area above the rear doors will adequately support a ceiling panel. Ideally, an additional ceiling brace is needed but since most vans don't have one this far back, an alternative arrangement must be used.

same way they were for the other panels. Then holes are drilled five inches apart along the entire length of the brace. (Make sure you hold the panel tight against the ceiling before drilling any holes.) After screws are installed in these holes, the other end of the panel must be dealt with. Here again, the screws are spaced about five inches apart. The only difference is in the drilling angle. Since the wall of the van is at an angle to the panel, the holes must be also drilled at an angle (Fig. 7-12). A good rule of thumb is to drill the holes at a right angle to the surface they will be anchored in. This won't always be possible but where it is, it's a good rule to follow.

The rear panel should present no problems. The panels in the middle of the ceiling should not be difficult either. That leaves one area to be covered. The front of the van. This area of the ceiling is the most difficult to panel.But it isn't so tough that it can't be handled by someone who has paneled the rest of the ceiling.

Many vans come with a panel screwed onto the ceiling directly above the front seats and extending to the windshield (Fig. 7-13). If your van did, the easiest way to deal with the front ceiling area in you van is to use that panel as a template. If you aren't using prefinished paneling and the panel that

Fig. 7-12. Since the area above the rear doors will be at an angle to the ceiling panel that is to be fastened to it, special attention must be given to the drilling of the mounting holes. Try to keep the drill at a right angle to the metal, not the ceiling panel. Drilling at an angle into a thin wood panel won't break a drill bit but drilling into metal at an angle can.

Fig. 7-13. If your van came with a factory-installed front ceiling panel like the one shown, the simplest way to cut a new one to the proper size is to use the old one as a template. (If the panel that came with the van is in good shape, consider just using it and covering it with whatever the rest of the ceiling is covered with.)

came with the van is in good shape, you might consider using it instead of cutting a new one. Of course, if you're using prefinished paneling you'll want to replace it so the front part of the ceiling will match the rest of the ceiling. But if you are going to cover the whole thing anyway, using the panel that came with the van could save you lots of work.

If your van didn't come with a panel above the front area of the van, you'll need to cut one yourself. First, measure the area to be covered. This figure will vary from conversion to conversion but most people panel the ceiling all the way to the windshield. If this is what you're going to do, measure from the center of the brace that is closest to the front of the van to the windshield (Fig. 7-14). This gives you the width of the panel needed. Now measure the width of the van. This gives you the length of the panel needed. Cut a panel to these dimensions.

Once you have the crude shape of the panel cut out, it is necessary to tailor it so it fits properly. Many vans will require a panel with curved corners. If yours does, the best way to do it is to eyeball it. To figure out the exact curve needed and draw it on the panel so you can cut it would take pretty heavy geometry. It's much simpler and faster to just eyeball it. Since the dimensions of the panel are not super critical, you can deviate from the ideal size by as much as three-quarter's of an inch and still be able to hide the mistake.

When you have the panel cut to size, the ceiling must be insulated. Then, mounting holes for any fixtures must be cut. Once that's done, the panel is ready to go up. The procedure for installing tne panel on the front part of the ceiling is very similar to the previous panels. There is a slight variation however. You'll notice that there is a lip that the front edge of the panel can be fitted into as shown in Fig. 7-15. This must be done before any holes are drilled. If you drill the holes before you push the panel into this lip, they won't line up properly. Once the edge of the panel is positioned however, the installation procedure is the same as the other panels. Holes are drilled along the entire length of the brace about five inches apart. Screws are installed in them and torqued down. And that's it. The panel is up.

Covering The Ceiling

Naturally, this step applies only if you have elected to use something other than prefinished paneling. If you are going to use something like upholstery material to cover the ceiling in your van, the installation is extremely simple. The only tools

Fig. 7-14. To measure the width of the front panel needed, take a reading from the center of the farthest forward ceiling brace to the lip where the panel will fit into.

Fig. 7-15. Usually the front edge of the panel can be hidden completely by fitting it into the lip above the windshield. Be sure to allow for this when deciding on the proper width of the front panel.

you'll need are a knife, tape measure, staple gun, and two extra hands. Again, a friend would come in very handy in this step. The extra hands are used to hold the material in place while it is stapled to the ceiling.

If the material you are using to cover the ceiling has a pattern on it, you must be careful to avoid distorting it. If lines are in the pattern, those lines should be straight after the material is in place. It is very easy to apply material to the ceiling in such a way that any lines wouldn't be straight, so keep an eye on the pattern as you go to make sure there are no problems. Start at the rear of the van. Cut the material around 4 inches wider than the width of the area to be covered. Allow about two inches to spare on either side to allow for any discrepancies in the installation. While your friend holds the material in place, smooth out any wrinkles from the center out and staple it to the ceiling. Don't worry about covering any mounting holes. The material can be cut away at a later time. Just concentrate on getting the material applied to the ceiling straight and unwrinkled. Use lots of staples. The material should be held tight against the ceiling everywhere. If it isn't, it may sag later. The staples should be around seven inches apart when you're through. Use more staples around the edge of any mounting holes. This will help hold the material in place while the fixtures are being installed.

When you get this far your ceiling should look very nice. In fact, the interior of your van should be taking definite shape.

Once you're satisfied with the job you did on upholstering the ceiling, the next step is to install the light fixtures you've allowed for. This is probably the simplest step in installing the ceiling. All that is needed is a screwdriver, some electrical tape, and a pair of cutters. If the mounting holes were covered over when you upholstered the ceiling, a utility knife is needed to trim away the material from that area.

If mounting instructions were supplied with the light fixtures you are going to install in the ceiling, follow them. But if there are none available you'll have to wing it. Depending on the type of fixture you're going to install, the possible hassles you're likely to run into will vary. If the fixtures are the simple bolt-on type, you're in luck. This type of fixture is the easiest to install. Simply connect the two wires to the fixture using the wire cutters and the electrical tape. If you really want to do it right, solder the connections. This makes a much better connection than simply twisting the two wires together. Then trim away any excess. Once that's done, tape the connection as tightly as you can making sure the two wires don't touch each other. If they do, a short will result. The safest way to do it is to first tape one connection up completely. Then wrap tape around both connections very tightly. This guarantees that there will be no contact between the two connections.

With both wires connected, the next step is the actual mounting of the fixture. A friend will come in handy during this step. Two hands are needed to hold the fixture in place while two more install the screws in the mounting holes. Once that's done, the installation is complete.

If the fixtures you've selected to mount in the ceiling are the flush-mount type, the installation is slightly more difficult. Once again, if mounting instructions were supplied with the fixture, you'd be wise to follow them. They've been written specifically for that unit by people who know what they are doing.

The electrical connections for a flush-mount fixture are the same as for a bolt-on type. Two wires must be connected. With that step behind you you're ready to mount the fixture. The unit that goes behind the ceiling is mounted first. Make sure the wires connected to the fixture are not pinched by the unit. They should be tucked back behind the unit completely out of sight. While holding the fixture in place, install the mounting screws. Then install the designer ring over the entire installation. Position it carefully so as to hide the rough cut around the unit. And that's it. The installation is complete.

Once you've installed the lights in your ceiling, that area of your conversion project is finished. If you've taken your time and exercised care over the various steps, the finished effect should be quite nice. If the area where the ceiling meets the wall looks a little rough, don't worry. That will be hidden later when you install molding. Now on to the installation of furniture and appliances.

Chapter 8

Furniture
and Appliances

With the walls and ceiling insulated and covered, the only major area of concern left to be dealt with is that of the inclusion of furniture and appliances. Of course what you install depends on what you will be using your van for. If you're into camping you'll probably want to include a refrigerator and possibly a stove. But if your van is to be used as simply a fun vehicle and not for overnight outings, the addition of these appliances may not be worth the added cost and work. A van converted for camping might include a table, bed and seating. But these items too could be eliminated if your van is to be just for cruising around. In this chapter the construction of various types of furniture is covered.

CAPTIONS FOR FOLLOWING 8-PAGE COLOR SECTION

Photo 1. Simple but elegent. The Vegas motif blends perfectly with the dark background, stirring images of a bubbling oasis under a pitch black desert sky.

Photo 2. This red gambling den awaits only a platinum silhouette against the wood grain paneling. Select your position at the poker table carefully though, for the mirror may cost you more hands than your intentions.

Photo 3. Tasteful striping accents the restrained elegance of this meticulously finished California jewel.

Photo 4. Regardless of the road it travels this loving space says trade winds. Natural materials and earth tones provide the Polynesian motif with functional beauty.

Photo 5. Brightly colored machine wizardry. A delight to any Dorothy's eye.

Photo 6. Follow the yellow brick road straight to fantasy.

Photo 7. The quad, rectangular style headlights and underslung fog lamps gives Penny Pincher plenty of blazing candlepower up front.

Photo 8 Inside, Penny Pincher shows a bunkhouse influence with lots of natural finished wood and little carpeting.

Photo 9. These horizontal stripes over the silver base lengthen the appearance of the van. Plus, a practical roof rack stands ready to be loaded for a quick getaway to the favorite campsite.

Among them are tables, beds, seats, and shelves. Also, the purchase and installation of several types of appliances is covered. Since not everyone will want to undertake the construction of the furniture they want to include in their van, the purchase and installation of readymade units is also covered.

The first step in installing either furniture or appliances is to decide exactly what you want to include. Make a list of everything you want in your van. Then make a tentative floor plan and work out the position of each major piece. For instance, if you've decided that you want a table, bed, and refrigerator in the back of your van, position them on paper before parting with any money or doing any cutting. It is important that you know for sure that everything you want to include will fit without seriously cramping the interior of the van. Once you've come up with a complete list and are sure that you know where you want to position each major piece, you're ready to begin the next phase—design. First, the furniture.

FURNITURE: CONSTRUCTED

With only a few basic tools and a little common sense you can construct furniture for your van that will be strong, lightweight, and attractive. Let's start with the construction of a table.

Building a Table

The simplest type of table to build is one that folds against the wall when not in use. The only materials needed are two hinges of suitable size, a piece of plywood of the size you want for the tabletop, about four feet of decorator chain, and sheet-metal screws. With these materials you can construct a table that is strong but highly functional. And when not in use, the table can fold against the wall and out of the way.

The first step is to cut a piece of plywood to size. It will serve as the actual table so the size of it is largely up to you. It should be large enough to be functional but not so large that it is difficult to live with. An excessively large table is going to be in the way when it is down and hard to fold up. The size of the table should be around four feet long and three feet wide. A minimum width of the tabletop is the distance from one vertical brace on the wall to another since the hinges supporting the table will have to be bolted directly to these

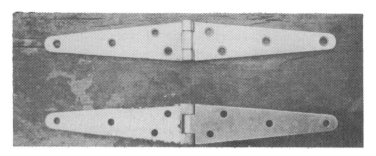

Fig. 8-1. Using a hinge that is this large makes for a very strong installation. If the table will not be supporting much weight, you could use a smaller type and lose nothing in the process.

braces. In most vans the minimum width for a fold-down table is around two feet. Any smaller than that and the edges of the table will fall short of the braces on the wall and make it impossible for the hinges to be mounted on them, thus weakening the table. To cut the tabletop a sabre saw or Skilsaw is used. Make the cuts as straight as possible because even though the edge of the table will be covered later, major variations in the cut will show up in the finished product.

The hinges needed to fasten the table to the wall are shown in Fig. 8-1. The actual shape of the hinges can vary considerably without affecting the application but they should be heavy-duty enough to support the table as well as anything that will ever be placed on it. If you plan to use the table as an extra seat, naturally you'll want to use heavy-duty hinges since light-duty hinges are not capable of supporting enough weight. There are countless styles of hinges available so select one that satisfies your personal taste. Just make sure it's strong enough to do the job.

To install the hinges you'll need a tape measure, screwdriver, and drill with an 1/8-inch drill bit. Using the tape measure, mark a line on the wall however many inches down from the ceiling you want the table to be. For instance, if you want the surface of the table to be fifty inches below the ceiling, mark a line 50 inches down from the top of the wall. The line need only be a short one—long enough to show the position of one hinge. Make sure the hinge is positioned low enough on the wall to allow the table to fold up against the wall without hitting the ceiling. If your table is to be 45 inches wide and you install the hinges 40 inches below the ceiling, you are going to run into problems. The table will not fold up against the wall because it will hit the ceiling first.

170

Fig. 8-2. Here the last few holes are being drilled to anchor the hinge in the wall. Next, the holes in the table surface are drilled and screws installed.

Once you've made a line for the first hinge, repeat the procedure and position the second hinge the proper number of inches down from the top of the wall. Be careful to keep your measurements accurate to ensure that the table will be parallel to the ceiling when you are finished.

With these lines made, you have established at what level the hinges are to be mounted. Now it is necessary to position the hinges horizontally. Remember that the hinges must be screwed directly into the vertical braces in the wall. If the braces are completely hidden you can locate them by lightly tapping the wall with a hammer and listening to the sound that is made. If you hit the wall where there is no brace a hollow sound will be heard. But if you hit the wall where there is a vertical brace it will feel solid and the sound made will likewise be solid. Tap the wall and locate two braces where the hinges are to be mounted. Using the tape measure (or yardstick) position hinge on the brace at the proper level so that the bottom flange can fold up. Then, while a friend holds it in place, drill several holes in the wall for the mounting screws. Most hinges have four mounting holes on either flange. Use all of them. Once you've drilled the holes, install sheet metal screws in them. Repeat this procedure for the other hinge.

The next step is to bolt the tabletop to the hinges. The hands of a friend are essential in this step. If you attempt to complete this step on your own you'll most likely screw up. Two hands are needed to hold the table-top in place and two hands are needed to drill mounting holes and install screws. Have a friend position the tabletop on the hinges as shown in Fig. 8-2.

Make sure the tabletop is centered on the hinges and is at least one half inch away from the wall. This is to allow adequate clearance for the molding or Formica later. While the tabletop is held firmly in place drill mounting holes into the topside of the tabletop and install screws in them. This is a tricky step so take your time. The table top should now be supported by the hinges. Fold it against the wall to see that it is straight and there are no problems. If there are none you're ready for the next step—the installation of the chain that will hold the table at a right angle to the wall. (Make sure the chain you use is heavy enough to support a person's weight if the table will double as a seat.)

Installing the chain is extremely simple as is evident in Fig. 8-3. Here again you'll need a friend's help. First install a hook in either side of the table. The chain will eventually be connected to these hooks so anchor them firmly. Now install a similar hook in either brace on the wall (the same braces that the hinges were bolted to). You'll need to first drill a hole here because the brace is metal and will not be penetrated simply by turning the hook by hand. Drill a hole that is slightly smaller than the diameter of the screw part of the hook. Then screw in the hook as far as possible. You're now ready to cut the chain to the proper length.

Hook one end of the chain to one of the hooks installed in the edges of the table. Run the chain to the respective hook on the wall and while a friend holds the table at a right angle to

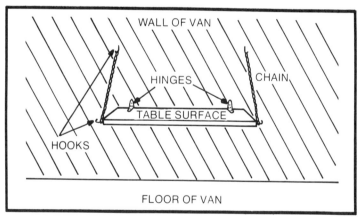

Fig. 8-3. To install the pieces of chain on the table four hooks are needed. One end of the chain is hooked to the wall. The other end is looped over the hook and installed in the corresponding edge of the table.

the wall, connect the chain to the hook on the wall. A carpenter's square would be very helpful in this step. It is needed in determining when the table is square to the wall. When you have one end of the chain connected to the table and the hook on the wall goes through the appropriate link to hold the table at a right angle, cut off all excess links. This procedure must be repeated for the other side. If, when you are finished, the table is not exactly square to the wall, the angle can be adjusted by using a different link in the chain over the hook on the wall. No latch is needed to hold the table in the up position when not in use. Just fold the table against the wall and hook the end of the chain to the wall on the closest link to the table possible. And the basic construction of the table is complete. All that remains are the esthetic touches. Since the tabletop is still naked plywood, you'll probably want to cover it with something. Formica, vinyl, paint, stain, all have been used before. One thing to consider when covering the table is the area of waterproofing. If the table will be used occasionally to hold items that might leak such as a water cooler, cans of beer, or any liquid, waterproofing the surface would be a good idea. There are several ways to go about it. One way is to cover the tabletop with Formica. It's available at most hardware stores. You'll need some contact cement to apply it to the surface of the table but that's all. Formica is completely waterproof and has the added advantages of being heat resistant, easy to clean and very durable.

If Formica is not the way you want to go you might consider painting the table and then coating it with special sealant. Again, the sealant is available at virtually all hardware stores and most lumber yards. It's marketed under names like Liquid Plastic and Spar-Var. It's similar to varnish but it dries clear and is more durable.

Another way to waterproof the table top is to cover it with vinyl contact paper. This is probably the cheapest way to go but it is also the least esthetically pleasing. It gives the table a "cheap" look so unless you just cannot go one of the other routes when waterproofing the surface of your table, avoid this method.

The underside of the table is another area that is pay dirt for esthetic design. When the table is folded against the wall the underside of the table will be all that shows. If you leave it natural it won't look very good. So treat it as if it were a canvas. Put a design there. Make it into an asset instead of a detriment.

To give your table an even nicer finished appearance install molding around the edge of it. This hides the cut in the plywood as well as making the tabletop look less "homemade." You might have to look a little harder for something to suit this purpose than you did for the waterproofing but it will be well worth your effort. Leaving the edge of the table bare will detract from the overall effect of your conversion job. Aluminum stripping is available at many hardware stores that would work perfectly for covering the edge of the table. It's pretty cheap and only takes small nails to install. (Contact cement also works quite well for applying it. Make sure that you allow adequate time for drying though or the stripping will peel off later.)

You'll never regret the time and effort it takes to build a table as described earlier. It will come in handy so often you'll wonder how you ever got by without it. And there are many other neat things you can build with only a small amount of money and a few tools that will be equally useful.

Building a Bed

As I said earlier, the addition of a bed to the back of your van could be a good thing or it could just be a waste. If you plan on sleeping only up to two people, the floor in your van could serve as a very nice bed after padding and carpet are installed. In fact, adding a bed would just encroach on the space available for living or other pieces of furniture. So don't add a bed just because you think it has to be done. Consider your needs. If you will be sleeping more than two people in your van at any one time a bed would be a very wise addition to your van. Depending on the style and position of the bed you want to include, you could sleep up to four people in your van quite comfortably.

There are two basic positions used in adding a bed. One is as shown in Fig. 8-4. The bed is positioned across the back of the van and covers the rear wheel wells. The second position is shown in Fig. 8-5. The bed is installed lengthwise against one of the walls.

Building and Installing a Bed Lengthwise

The simplest type of bed to build and install uses the same basic design as the table covered earlier. The chains are

174

Fig. 8-4. With the bed installed across the back of the van as shown, the rear doors are not as easily accessed; however, lots of storage space is created, the wheel wells are hidden, and a bed is available.

replaced by legs since added strength is necessary. The surface of the bed must naturally be padded. But basically the construction parallels that of the table. Fig. 8-5 shows how it's done.

The first step is to decide on the size of the bed. This is an area where personal preference is the main determinant. This type of bed will only sleep one person so figure your measurements based on that fact. For instance, if you don't toss and turn much at night you could probably build the bed only three feet wide and still be comfortable. But if you are a restless sleeper you'll probably want to make it wider than that. In addition to the bed's width the length must also be considered. If you're of average height a bed six feet long should be adequate.

Once you've arrived at the basic dimensions of the bed you're ready to cut a piece of plywood to that size. The plywood should be 3/4 of an inch thick. Any thinner than that and the bed simply will not be able to support the amount of weight it will run into. After you've cut the plywood to size sand the edges to eliminate any sharp edges or splinters. The next step is to decide at what height the bed will be installed. Bear in mind that the bed can double as extra seating. If the bed is installed too high on the wall it will be uncomfortable to sit on. An ideal height for sitting is the distance between the bottom of the foot and the bend at the knee. Again, since you have no way of knowing the sizes of the people who will be sitting on the bed, this measurement must be approximated. Two feet from the floor should be just about right for most people.

Now for the hinges. Since the amount of weight the bed will have to support is much greater than that of the table, naturally the hinges will need to be much stronger. Cost increases with size so expect to pay more when you go to make your purchase. A hardware store should be able to supply you with hinges of suitable size. In fact, you can most likely get the same style of hinge you used for the table. The only difference will be that of size. Try to keep the hinges matching; it adds a note of professionalism to your conversion job. An additional set of hinges will be needed for the legs since they too will have to fold out of the way when the bed is not in use. The hinges needed for the legs can be much smaller than those needed for the bed surface; a set of simple butt hinges should work quite nicely. Don't use anything smaller than two inches though or you'll run into problems. Very small hinges wear out very fast when used where a larger hinge is needed.

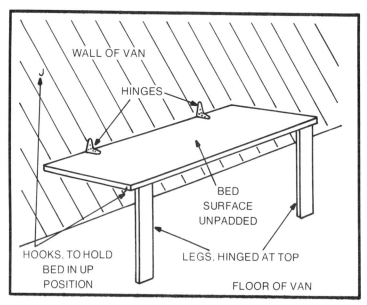

Fig. 8-5. With the bed installed along one wall the rear doors are easily accessible but other restrictions arise. The bed is only wide enough for one person; no storage space is available; and the wheel wells must still be dealt with.

The material needed for the legs is another area of personal preference. Probably the most popular material is simple two-by-fours. They are strong, very cheap, and can be dressed up quite nicely. They are also easier to work with than the other materials that would also fit the application.

OK. We have the leg material, hinges, and bed surface. It's time for construction. The first step is the installation of the two large hinges that will support the bed surface. The installation procedure is the same as the one for the table. The hinges must be positioned in such a way that they are bolted to one of the vertical braces on the wall. If you've decided on a bed height of two feet the hinges should be installed two inches less than that from the floor. (That's to allow for the bed surface and the padding that somes later.) They should also be positioned far enough apart to afford adequate support for the entire length of the bed. For instance, if the two hinges were installed only two feet apart, that leaves four feet of the bed that is not supported. But if the hinges are positioned four feet apart (a foot in from either end) the strength of the bed is dramatically increased. Remember the hinges must be anchored in the metal vertical braces.

Once you've installed the hinges the next step is to conquer the problem of the legs. If you are going to use two by fours this task is relatively simple. You'll need two legs that are as long as the distance the hinges are from the floor. (for added strength you might consider installing three legs as shown in Fig. 8-6.) The legs are connected to the bed with two smaller hinges. But first consider dressing them up a bit. This can be done by staining them, painting them, or covering them. Here's an idea. Take a hatchet and make lots of nicks in the legs to give a hand-hewn look. Then rub Danish walnut oil into the legs. The finished effect will be a rustic appearance. If a rustic look doesn't suit your interior design you might consider painting the legs. First sand the legs until they have rounded edges. This is to eliminate that two by four look. Next, using a high quality spray paint, paint the legs very carefully. If you hurry through this step the paint may run, causing the legs to look very bad. Avoid using a low-quality spray paint. It will be harder to get a nice finish if you do and the paint will be less glossy. Low-quality spray paints tend to run much more readily than do quality spray paints.

Once the legs are finished they must be bolted to the bed surface. This is not hard but it would help to have a friend's

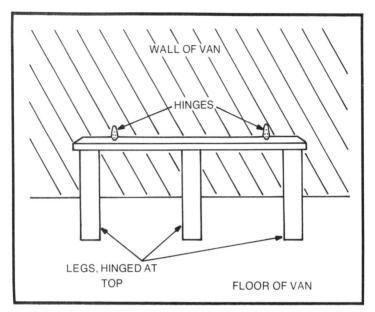

Fig. 8-6. Installing a third leg centered between the other two legs adds much more strength. The extra time involved in doing so is minimal. Three legs should make the bed strong enough to support anything short of twenty people.

assistance. First the hinges are bolted to the underside of the bed. Their position is far less critical than that of the hinges that support the bed so you can probably get by with simply eyeballing it. The hinges should be installed in such a way that the leg can be folded against the underside of the bed when it is not in use. If you put the hinge on backwards this will not be possible so make sure you get it right the first time. Next the legs are bolted to the hinges. This is where a friend will come in handy. Have him hold the leg in place while you drill the necessary mounting holes. Then install the mounting screws. And that's it. The leg is installed. Repeat this for the other leg(s).

The next step is going to be a little difficult so proceed slowly. The bed surface must be bolted to the hinges you've installed on the wall. While a friend holds the bed in the correct position drill the mounting holes in the topside of it and install the necessary mounting screws through the hinges. Make sure the bed is not cocked relative to the wall or it will be crooked when it is folded against the wall. Also, be absolutely certain that you allow adequate clearance between the bed and the wall for the padding that is to come later. If you install the bed so that it is butted up against the wall in the down position you won't be able to fold it up out of the way because the padding will prevent it. There should be about an inch and a half clearance between the bed and the wall. Of course if you plan on heavily padding the bed, you must allow more clearance. The important thing to remember is that the finished product must fold up against the wall. If there is no clearance between the wall and the edge of the bed this will not be possible.

To hold the ends of the legs in place while the bed is in use, wood screws are installed directly into the floor. Lower the bed in position and square the legs relative to the bed. Then drill a hole directly in front of either leg and directly behind it. Install the wood screws in these holes. They will keep the end of the leg from getting kicked from under the bed while it is in use. Make sure you screw the wood screws in far enough so that they are not in the way. They need only extend far enough above the surface of the floor to hold the leg in place.

All that remains to do now is pad the bed and take care of any little esthetic changes necessary to make the bed look like a professional installation. The amount of padding you elect to use for the bed is another area of personal preference but an average amount is around an inch and a half. This may not sound like much but it is plenty to make the bed comfortable. If you are used to sleeping on a very soft bed you'll want to increase that figure accordingly. The type of padding to use is white foam. It's the cheapest kind available and it works as well as anything. It's available at most upholstery shops. To apply it to the surface of the bed there are several methods. One is stapling. This is a quick and easy way to fasten the padding to the bed. Unfortunately it leaves indentations in the surface of the bed where the staples are installed. So if you want the finished product to look absolutely flat, stapling is not the way to go. Another cheap and easy way to fasten the padding to the bed is contact cement. It's not as quick and easy as stapling but it leaves no indentations. And it secures the padding much more firmly than staples can.

There are many types of material available with which to cover the padding. I used vinyl upholstery material once. That was a mistake. In hot weather the vinyl is very uncomfortable to sleep on. It sticks to the body. A much better material would be a thick cotton. This provides more ventilation and is thus cooler to sleep on. This is also available at upholstery shops at an average cost of around $4 a square yard. Two square yards should be more than adequate. To install the covering material over the padding you'll run into some more problems. Contact cement can't be used because there is nothing solid to glue the material to. Staples can't be used since this would leave deep indentations making the bed uncomfortable to sleep on. One solution is to fasten the covering material to the edges of the bed only. The seam can be hidden by using the same type of molding used in covering the edge of the table. First, lay the material over the padding and smooth out any wrinkles. Then, using small carpet tacks or staples attach one edge of the material to the side of the bed. For instance you might want to start with the side edge of the bed. Tack the material to this edge firmly. Then do the *opposite* end smoothing out wrinkles and pulling the material tight as you go. Next the front edge of the bed is covered. Be sure to pull the material tight before tacking it down. The last edge you do should be the one closest to the wall. To do this the bed must be folded against the wall and the material tacked from underneath.

Once you've tacked the material down on all sides you're ready to install the molding. If you've also installed a table in your van, with molding around the edge, try to use the same kind around the edge of your bed. It's always better to keep molding and the hinges matching whenever possible. After the molding is installed around the entire perimeter of the bed a fastening system for keeping the bed in the up position when folded against the wall must be designed. This can be done by using four simple hooks and a foot of chain. When the bed is in the up position install four hooks as shown in Fig. 8-7. Then cut two pieces of chain to a length that will, when connected to the hooks hold the bed tight against the wall. When you want to use the bed the chain is simply disconnected from the edge of the bed. The bed is then lowered into position. Simple.

The basic installation of this type of bed is complete. However you might want to do something with the underside of the bed as with the table. As it stands now when the bed is folded against the wall an unfinished piece of plywood shows (the underside of the bed). There are a number of ways to handle this. One is to paint a mural on the plywood. Or cover it with mirrors. Both ideas have been used with stunning results.

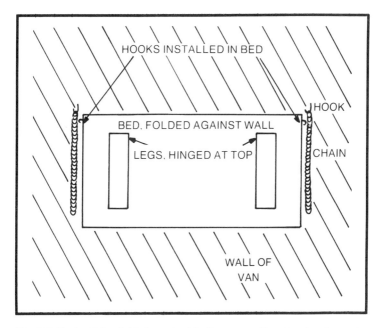

Fig. 8-7. To hold the fold-down bed in the up position, two hooks are installed in either end of the bed as shown, just as they were for the table. One end of the chain is fastened to the wall by a hook. When the bed must be held against the wall, it is simply folded up and the chains are connected to the hooks.

This approach to the problem of hiding the underside of the bed is an ideal one because you are doing two things at once. Not only are you hiding an ugly piece of wood but you are supplying your van with something that looks nice. If you decide to paint a mural on the underside of the bed, when it is in the up position it will look like just a piece of art. If you choose the mirror route, people will freak out when you unhook it and fold it down to expose a bed. So it is clear that this approach to hiding the underside of the bed is a good one.

Building a Bed Crosswise

Constructing a bed to fit crosswise in the back of your van is more difficult than the design just covered. But it has it's own advantages. With a bed crosswise in the van, space is created below it where storage compartments can be installed. Also with this style of bed, two people can comfortably sleep together where with the other style only one person can be accomodated. So there are definite reasons for

181

going with this type of installation as opposed to the previous one.

If you've installed a partition of the same design as the one covered in Chapter 6, the following bed design cannot be followed exactly. No door to the storage area can be built since the partition will block this area. The storage area can only be accessed from the rear of the van through the rear doors. With modification a door could be installed but that modification is so extensive that the relative advantages of such a project are greatly lessened.

The first step, as it was with the previous construction project, is to decide how big you want the bed. Naturally you'll want to hide the two rear wheel wells but there are other dimensions that must be decided on. For instance how high should the bed be from the floor? Again, this is an area of personal preference. If you plan on storing large objects under the bed, objects that require lots of clearance, you'll want to make the bed higher than usual. But if you'll be storing the average fare of tools, luggage, a jack, etc. the height of the wheel wells should be adequate. Another dimension that must be decided on is how far forward will the bed extend. Most beds of this design extend only forward enough to hide the rear wheel wells but your application may require a variation of this pattern. Consider your sleeping habits. If the bed needs to extend beyond the rear wheel wells in order to sleep you comfortably, that's ok. The primary determinant is sleeping comfort. Let that be your overriding consideration.

Figure 8-8 shows the basic construction of a bed designed to be installed across the rear of the van and hiding the rear wheel wells. As you can see it is a pretty simple design. In fact the only materials you'll need are a sheet of 3/4-inch plywood, about ten feet of two by fours, and several hinges (for the door on the storage compartment). Of course you'll need the standard odds and ends like a tape measure, screws, a saw, and a screwdriver. But once these things are collected you're ready to begin.

Assuming you've already decided on the size of the bed surface, the next step is to cut a piece of plywood to that size. That piece will serve as the surface of the bed. The remaining piece of 3/4-inch plywood will be used for the door to the storage compartment so don't pitch it. Test fit the piece of plywood you cut for the surface of the bed. Make sure that it

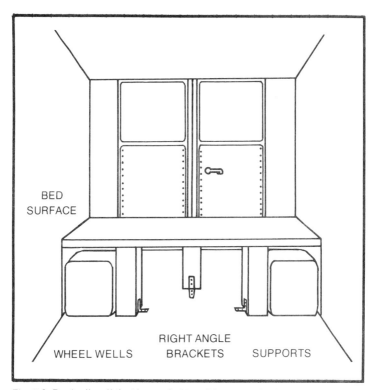

BED
SURFACE

RIGHT ANGLE
WHEEL WELLS   BRACKETS   SUPPORTS

Fig. 8-8. Basically, all that is needed to add a crosswise bed to your van is a sheet of plywood of the proper dimensions and a few two by four supports. Note that the wheel wells are effectively hidden with this type of installation.

fits snugly. It doesn't need to actually contact the walls of the van but it should come very close. Once you are satisfied with that piece, set it aside. Now you're ready to deal with the supports for the bed. If your van is an early Econoline there are two braces in either rear corner that can serve as ideal supports for the rear end of the bed as shown in Fig. 8-9. But if your van doesn't have these braces, you'll need to fashion your own. It's really quite simple. First, cut a piece of two by four to the length that is required to make your bed the height you've decided on. For instance, if you want the finished bed to be two feet from the floor of the van, cut the two by four supports to a length of 23 1/4 inches. These legs will serve as the supports for the rear end of the bed. Two more are needed for the forward end of the bed. (If you selected a height for the bed that corresponds with the height of the rear wheel wells, there is no need to make two forward supports because the tops of the wheel wells can serve as supports themselves.)

With four two by four legs cut to the proper length the next step is to position the large piece of plywood that will serve as the surface of the bed where it will be permanently installed. Now this is a tricky step. The two by four legs must be positioned in such a way that the weight the bed will support in the future is evenly distributed. In some installations it may be necessary to use more than four supports. For instance, it may prove necessary to install one in the very center of the bed surface. You'll have to experiment a little here. But the most common placement of the supports is about seven inches in from the edges of the bed in each corner. In the case of the forward supports the wheel wells may not make it feasible to position the legs seven inches in from the edges of the bed. If this is the case in your van, build up the tops of the wheel wells so they can serve as supports themselves, thus eliminating any need for the front two by four supports.

Once you've decided on the placement of all the supports they must be permanently fixed in position. There are several ways to do this. One is to nail them in place by driving nails through the top part of the bed down into the supports. Another is to use screws and right angle brackets as shown in Fig. 8-10. The latter technique makes for a much more solid installation and I recommend you go with that procedure. Nails have a tendency to weaken and loosen under strain. Screws don't.

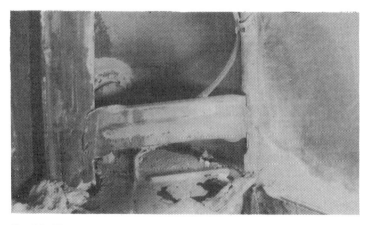

Fig. 8-9. The rear corner braces in Econolines are at an ideal height to be used a supports in most applications. The bed surface simply rests on the brace in each corner.

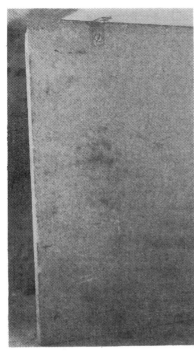

Fig. 8-10. Right-angle brackets are installed at the bottom as well as the top of each bed support to hold them in place. Here an individual compartment has been incorporated into the storage area under the bed so a divider instead of just a two by four support has been used.

Work with one leg at a time. Check the position of the bed surface. When it is exactly right have a friend hold one of the supports in position and install a screw through the surface of the bed down into the support. One screw should be enough to hold it in place during the next step. Right angle brackets should be installed as shown in Fig. 8-10 at both the top of the support and the bottom. (You'll find that the right angle brackets you install on the bottom of the support are much easier to screw into place than the ones at the top.)

Once the supports are in place and the surface of the bed is firmly anchored, the next project is installing a door to hide the underside of the bed from the front. This step is a little difficult so proceed slowly. First, measure the opening that needs to be covered. Measure it very carefully so that the door will fit properly. The door should fit under the surface of the bed, not against it. Then, cut a piece of 3/4-inch plywood to these dimensions. This piece will be the actual door. Test fit it to see that it is of the proper size. If it is the next step is to install the hinges. This is most difficult step in installing a bed. If the hinges are not positioned exactly right the door

185

will not open easily. It will bind against itself. This step is almost impossible to accomplish correctly without a friend helping. The plywood should be positioned over the opening it will cover. As one person holds the plywood in place the other person is free to install the hinges. They should be positioned in such a way that the load of the door is distributed evenly. If you are using three hinges for the door, the two end hinges should be installed approximately a foot from either side of the bed and the third hinge should be centered on the door. After the hinges have been installed open and close the door to see that it works properly. If it does, you're ready to move on to the next step. If it doesn't adjust the position of the hinges slightly until the door opens and closes freely.

To keep the bottom of the door from getting pushed back under the bed and thus ripping the hinges loose it is necessary to install stops in the floor of the van. This is extremely simple to do. All that is needed is a couple of fairly large wood screws and a screwdriver. Close the door on the bed and make a mark on the floor where the bottom of the door falls as shown in Fig. 8-11. Then open the door and have a friend support it so that it is out of the way. Then make another line 3/4 of an inch closer to the rear of the van than the first line. The two big wood screws should be installed close to the walls of the van on this line. They will serve as stops and prevent the bottom of the

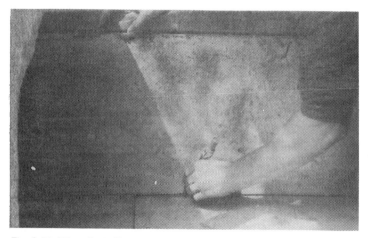

Fig. 8-11. When installing a door to the storage area under the bed, a line is drawn on the floor where the door will fall. This is to aid in the placement of the stops that are necessary to keep the door from getting pushed too far under the bed.

186

door from getting shoved under the bed. Position the two screws about five feet apart for maximum effect (Fig. 8-16). And that completes the basic installation. But there are still a few loose ends that must be dealt with. First, a method must be devised where the door to the storage area can be supported other than by human hands when in the up position. The easiest way to accomplish this is by using a small length of chain of the same type used in supporting the fold-down table. One end is attached to the wall at one end of the door; the other end of the chain attaches to a hook that is installed on the edge of the door. When the door must be supported the chain is simply connected to the hook on the door. Simple.

One area remains to tackle. Esthetics. The basic bed is constructed but it doesn't look very good and it won't be very comfortable to sleep on in its present condition. But with very little effort it can be transformed from an ungainly construction project into a nice piece of furniture via padding and upholstery material. Let's start with the bed surface.

First it is necessary to select a thickness of padding. One inch is the most common thickness used for beds in vans. Then there remains the purely esthetic decision of what to cover the padding with. Select an upholstery material that is both durable and comfortable to sleep on. You'll need approximately four square yards of it, depending on the size of your bed. Don't neglect the area of the door to the storage area though. It too must be covered. If you intend to do it in the same pattern as you use for the bed, add another yard to the amount of upholstery material needed.

The padding is installed over the surface of the bed using contact cement. First trim the padding to the proper size. Then, while a friend helps to smooth out any wrinkles, glue it to the surface of the bed. It doesn't need to be firmly anchored; just so it won't slip when the bed is in use. Next comes the upholstery material. This step must be done much more carefully than the padding step since any mistakes made will show in the finished product. Cut the upholstery material to a size that is three inches longer than the surface of the bed in every direction. That extra three inches is essential so that it can be tacked to the underside of the bed later. When you have a piece of the proper size lay it over the surface of the bed as squarely as possible. Smooth out any wrinkles. While a friend holds one edge of the upholstery material still, working from the opposite edge, pull the material tight and tack it to the underside of the bed. Be sure that the material is kept as square to the bed as possible throughout this step. The material can be tacked to the underside of the bed by using a staple gun or carpet tacks. With one edge tacked down, you can now work on the opposite edge, the edge that the friend was holding. Again, pull the material tight keeping it square and tack the edge to the underside of the bed. Now the same procedure must be followed in tacking the remaining two edges of the upholstery material to the underside of the bed. Once that's done the bed should be pretty comfortable to lie on. As an added touch you might want to install upholstery buttons on the bed surface. Fig. 8-12 shows what this looks like. It's really quite simple. A scrap of the material is taken to an upholstery shop where buttons are made from it. These buttons are mounted on the ends of nails so you can guess the installation procedure. The button is simply hammered into place. It must be done very carefully though to avoid damaging the material that covers the button. The position and depth to which the buttons are hammered are matters left to personal discretion. This project will cost around three dollars and take about an hour and a half to do right but the surface of your bed will look very professional as a result.

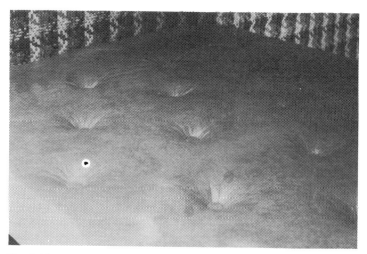

Fig. 8-12. Adding upholstery buttons to your bed surface may look hard but really it is very simple. If you can drive a nail straight, you can install buttons like these. The hardest part is positioning them relative to each other. A pattern must be developed and adhered to.

Covering the door to the compartment is accomplished in the same manner as covering the bed. The padding goes on first and is followed by a piece of upholstery material that has been cut three inches too large in every direction. It's tacked down and that's it. As a further finishing touch you might consider installing a decorator handle on the door to make it easier to open. They can be found in all hardware stores in just about every imaginable style and color.

So that's how a bed is installed crosswise in the back of the van. The ugly wheel wells are hidden and lots of seating area is provided at the same time.

Constructing a Shelf

Probably the easiest thing to construct in the back of a van is a shelf. Just about any hunk of wood will serve the purpose and the only other hardware necessary are two angle brackets and some screws. The procedure is simple. The wood (preferably 1/2-inch plywood) is cut to the desired size. Then the right angle brackets are installed on the appropriate wall at an equal height to each other from the floor. Then the piece of plywood is screwed into place. And that's it. Instant shelf. The shelf can be painted, carpeted, stained, mirrored, flocked, just about anything you want to do with it. To make it match the rest of the decor of your van try using the same type of upholstery material you used to cover the bed to cover the shelf. This gives a nice coordinated look. Also it's dandy a way to use some of the scraps left over from covering the bed.

If you're into a little more elaborate shelf you might consider installing one that is flush-mounted in the wall. This type of shelf is much more difficult to construct than the first type mentioned but it looks very nice. To do it you'll need to cut a hole in that nice wall you installed. You'll have to cut right through the padding, covering material, and the insulation. If you can bring yourself to do that then you're set.

First decide on how big an area you want to cut out of your wall. Since the vertical braces in the wall cannot be altered without weakening the structure of the van, you'll need to keep the width of the area down to around 24 inches. As to the height of the area to be cut out, you're really unlimited. When you've arrived at the size of the area you want to cut out, drill a hole within that area in the wall. This is to get the blade of the saw through the plywood wall. Using a sabre saw, keyhole saw, or other suitable cutting device, cut the hole to the proper dimensions. Remove all the insulation from this area and any sawdust. Next cut a piece of plywood to fit along each edge of the hole as shown in Fig. 8-13. It should fit snugly between the plywood wall and the metal wall. When it's cut to the proper size, install screws in the positions shown in Fig. 8-13. Install each piece following this procedure. When you're done you'll have an area in your wall that is sunken in. Now add planks for shelves and that's it. The plywood can be finished with whatever suits your interior decor.

Tables, beds, shelves, all easy to design and construct. But if doing-it-yourself isn't your bag, don't fret. With cash you can buy something that is equally suited to your needs as hand-built furniture would be. Let's look at what's available.

FURNITURE: PURCHASED

If the idea of building your own furniture doesn't suit you but you still want to include some furniture in your van

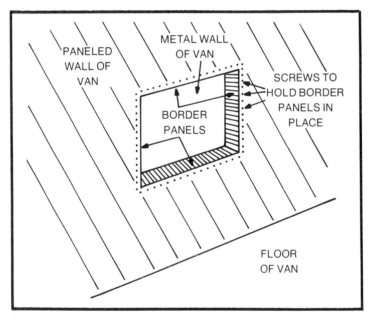

Fig. 8-13. Border panels are installed along each side of the cut out area. Screws are added to hold the panels in place. They are installed through the wall panel and into the border panel. The border panels should fit snugly between the metal wall of the van and the wall panel for maximum strength.

Fig. 8-14. If building-it-yourself is not the way you want to handle the seating and sleeping problem, a unit like this marketed by Van Mail in Wheeling, Illinois may better suit you. As well as serving as a couch, the unit folds down to form an adequate size bed. (Courtesy of Van Mail.)

prepare yourself to shell out some money. The type of furniture you want to include is probably available but naturally it will cost considerably more than building it yourself.

The most common piece of store-bought furniture for vans is the all-in-one unit as shown in Fig. 8-14. This specific unit is marketed by Van Mail. Not only does it serve as extra seating but it can be folded into a large bed in a matter of seconds. It's sold with a table with a Formica surface and is a beautiful addition to any interior. So if you want to include a bed, table, and bench seats in your van this all-in-one unit is one way to go. It will require a little do-it-yourselfing on your part because it is made to install over the rear wheel wells but the installation steps have been kept simple to avoid as many hassles as possible.

Wood Fabricators in Elkhart, Indiana markets a similar unit. The combo unit shown in Fig. 8-15 is of lighter construction than the unit marketed by Van Mail and is less versatile but still offers a wide range of functions for a reasonable price. Here again a table can be purchased that is designed to complement the unit. The biggest difference between the unit available from Wood Fabricators and the one from Van Mail is that the latter does not include a floor. But the combo unit marketed by Wood Fabricators includes two long couches designed to fit up against either wall in a van in addition to a floor covered with linoleum. The couches are hinged to the floor so when the unit is installed the couches are folded forward over the floor. When the unit is in place the couches are simply folded out against the walls of the van. Clever and simple. The Wood Fabricators unit has the added advantage of being able to be purchased a component at a time. That is, one of the couches could be purchased and the rest of the set could be installed at a later time with no hassles. This is a big advantage for the person who doesn't have a large sum of money to shell out all in one whack.

In addition to bed, seat, and table combinations there are many varieties of kitchen cabinets and bars available that are equally simple to install. Some come with sinks and stoves

Fig. 8-15. A similar unit to that in Fig. 8-14 is manufactured by Wood Fabricators in Elkhart, Illinois. This unit even includes a floor for your van; something the Van Mail unit does not. The Wood Fabricators' unit is of slightly lighter construction than Van Mail's, but it is also more comprehensive.

incorporated in them and others are even more elaborate with wine racks, ice crushers, and chopping blocks. As you might guess, the prices of these units are equally fantastic. But with an unlimited pail of money a van could be outfitted to be no less impressive than something one might see aboard the Starship Enterprise!

When shopping for prefabricated furniture you alone are charged with the responsibility of selecting a unit that is worth what you pay for it. Not all manufacturers are as reputable as some I've mentioned. In fact, some are marketing units that are intended to hold together only long enough to be installed in a van, so it is important that you proceed cautiously. Here are a few things to look for. First, when selecting a couch/bed combination that is made of wood examine the joints carefully. Some manufacturers use only the cheapest and fastest type of joint while others are interested in turning out a strong unit. The joint should not simply be glued. If it's a high-quality unit it will also be screwed. Don't settle for nails. Furniture held together with glue and nails is not intended to last for any length of time. But furniture that uses screws to hold the joints together is built for strength. So let that be one determinant. Screws, not nails.

Next, the type of joint is important. Some manufacturers use a simple butt joint as shown in Fig. 8-16. A much better joint is the dado, also shown in Fig. 8-16. A butt joint cannot withstand any flexing and is not intended to. In fact the butt joint has no place in the furniture manufacturing business. The dado joint is designed to not weaken under strain and affords much more strength than does the simple butt joint.

Don't settle for the salesman folding and unfolding the seat/bed combo. Try it yourself. A salesman has lots of time to practice and make it look easy. The real test is for you to do it. If you can unfold and fold a bed/seat combo quickly and easily then you are assured that the unit can do what it has been designed to do. Open and close the unit several times. Pay special attention to how smooth the unit operates. If it binds or is hard to move at times, chances are the design of that unit wasn't given the consideration it should have been. Have the salesman give you a detailed demonstration of all the functions possible with that unit. If the ad says it can be folded to seat five people ask to see how it's done. Remember: you must protect yourself. Don't assume that the salesman is looking out

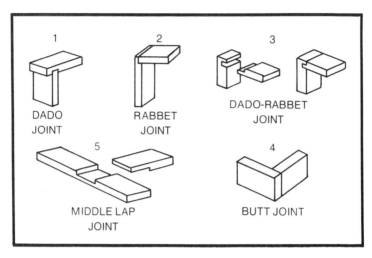

Fig. 8-16. The sturdiest type of joint shown here is the dado joint, but any of these are preferable to the simple butt joint, which weakens very quickly when under stress. The dado joint, if used correctly, should never weaken.

for your best interest because quite often he will be concerned with only the best interests of the company that employs him.

Examine the hinges on the unit. These little metal things will probably take more strain than the rest of the unit combined. If they are not firmly anchored they could rip loose under normal use. If the basic construction material of the unit is particle board or some other manmade wood-based material chances are the hinges haven't been adequately anchored. But if the unit is constructed using plywood there should be no problem with the hinges. Either way, the hinges should be of a size that is capable of handling the strain it will run into. If the hinges are used to enable an entire couch to hinge forward they should be no less than an inch and a half in length and held on by at least six screws.

Examine carefully how the upholstery material is fastened to the basic unit. It should be tacked down at least every three inches. If it is held in place by only a tack every foot the unit is inferior. Upholstery material on these units is what takes the strain of countless people sitting and sleeping on the unit. If it is not firmly anchored chances are it will pull loose around the edges later. If the material has been glued around the edges of the unit that's fine. Glue will hold just as well as tacks if it has been applied properly. Examine the actual upholstery material. If it is a display model you are being shown look for snags and dirt spots left by previous customers. That will give you an idea of what to expect as far as longterm wear is concerned. If the material has many snags in it be alerted to the fact that type of material may not be suited for use by children. You'll need something a little more childproof. Many of the couches and beds manufactured today are treated with ScotchGuard, a very effective protective treatment for cloth. Other techniques are used to further increase the material's resistance to dirt, moisture, and snags so ask the salesman about them. And if he doesn't have the answers forego any decision regarding the purchase of the unit until you get them.

A final point to consider when selecting a bed/seat unit is that of personal application. Make absolutely certain that the unit will do what you want it to do and will fit in your particular van. Some units marketed as "universally fitting" turn out to be less than that in the actual installation so you'd be wise to take a few measurements. Many times a unit will be designed to be installed in a particular make and model van; if that corresponds with your van no measurements are necessary. But if you are considering the purchase of a unit that has no specific application called out, measure the length and width of the unit to make absolutely certain that it will fit in your van.

If you're in the market for cabinets for your van there are several places that you should pay special attention to in the construction of the unit. If the cabinet you are interested in includes drawers, you have an excellent indicator of the overall quality of the unit. Very few manufacturers give adequate consideration to the problem of building sturdy drawers. Usually they fit so tightly that closing and opening them is a real chore or the basic construction techniques are at such a low level that the drawer simply doesn't hold up under strain. By carefully examining how the drawer mechanism is constructed you get a fairly good idea as to what degree of quality the rest of the unit has been constructed.

When selecting a cabinet for your van it is again important to examine the type of joint used in its construction. A dado joint is much better than a simple butt joint for already covered reasons. So let that knowledge affect your decision. The doors to the cabinet should close tightly but easily. If the cabinet has been designed for use in vans it will probably have some kind of mechanism for keeping the door closed while the van is in transit. If it doesn't the door will keep popping open as you are rolling down the road.

The van accessories market has turned into a highly competitive field and will get even more so. If you take the time to shop around you can usually get a better deal than if you were to go to the nearest supplier and plunk down the hard cash. Prices are being undercut daily so use that fact to your advantage. Do some comparison shopping.

APPLIANCES

Selecting appliances for your van will be a simpler task than selecting prebuilt furniture because there are fewer areas to check. There are several big manufacturers that will stand behind their product because they are too big not to. They have a reputation to uphold. One such manufacturer is Norcold, probably the biggest supplier of van refrigerators in operation. Their units have earned the reputation of exceptionally high quality and dependability. They offer models that are specifically designed to be installed in the rear of a van. They even have units that are specially suited to cabinet installations.

When judging the quality of an appliance many of the same rules apply that did for the selection of furniture. Special areas to examine carefully are the door hinges, the plastic appointments inside the unit, and the quality of finish. By making a detailed inspection of these areas you can usually get a very good idea of the quality of that unit. First, let's deal with the selection of heaters for vans.

HEATERS

Most of us are used to putting up with little annoyances like rattles, squeaks, and sticky levers, but few of us are accustomed to hardships like being cold, tired, or hungry. Until recently the van owner had to rely completely on the factory-installed heater to keep the occupants warm. But there are units available that effectively heat an entire van. No longer is it necessary to put up with the hardship of being cold. You'll just have the squeaks and rattles to contend with.

The type of heater I am speaking of uses the hot water from the van's cooling system to heat the rear area. This type

196

Fig. 8-17. Since most factory-installed heaters are not adequate to heat the rear area of a van, Hellstar Corp. manufactures a unit that is designed to fill that gap. By using the hot water from the van's cooling system, this heater can effectively warm even a very large van. The unit is small, making it easy to install in most vans.

of heater is extremely simple to connect. One such unit, manufactured by Hellstar Corporation of Wahoo, Nebraska, (Fig. 8-17) requires only two connections for operation. It can put out 15,000 Btus per hour which is pretty incredible considering its size—only eight inches high, eight inches wide, and eight inches deep. Being this small makes it possible to incorporate this unit into many different places—under a seat or bed, behind a wheel well. The unit is a little expensive—around $100 at the time of publication; but if you will be using your van where it gets cold, this unit would be a very nice addition to your van. Also it's the kind of modification that substantially increases the value of your finished van. If and when you decide to sell, you can extoll the advantages of having an auxiliary heater in the rear part of the van to the prospective buyer.

Hellstar also markets another handy appliance—a hot water heater. If you've been camping in your van and have run into the problems that all campers face, you'll really appreciate having hot water available to you even in the wild. The unit, shown in Fig. 8-18, holds only three gallons so it's not for taking baths or showers. But it's ideal for things like washing dishes and laundry, making coffee, or just general cleaning. It only takes fifteen minutes for the unit to heat three gallons from 60° to 140° so even if you need lots of water, you won't have to wait long. The hot water heater is a little cheaper than the space heater, selling for $75 at the time of publication. But hot water in the back of a van is a real luxury while camping. Heaters are available from Hellstar Corporation at 1600 Chestnut Street in Wahoo, Nebraska, 68066.

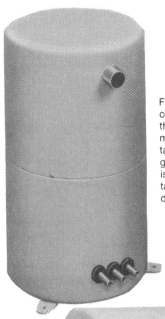

Fig. 8-18. The hot water from the cooling system is used again by this hot water heater also manufactered by Hellstar Corp. It takes only 15 minutes to heat 3 gallons of water to 140°. The unit is available as vertical or horizontal standing to further facilitate different mounting places.

ICEBOXES AND REFRIGERATORS

Buying an icebox is simple. Since the construction of iceboxes is far less complicated than refrigerators there are less areas to check out.

Iceboxes

Iceboxes, as the name implies, use ice to keep food cold. There are no compressors or gases involved, only a big hunk of ice. In fact there is really no difference between an ice chest used for picnics and a typical icebox designed for the rear of vans.

When selecting an icebox the most important thing to check is the basic construction of the unit. American Formed

Fig. 8-19. A block of ice is used to keep the food cold. As it melts, the water drains out through a built-in drain pipe. (Courtesy of American Formed Plastics, Inc.)

Plastics in Elkhart, Indiana markets several models that are good examples of quality in construction (Fig. 8-19). Since the units are so simple, there really isn't much involved in making them sturdy. But not all manufacturers take the time even to do that. The AFPC unit is solid and should give trouble-free service when properly taken care of. The ice sits on the upper shelf. As it melts, the water drains out through a drain tube installed in the shelf. The door lock is flushmounted. The door itself is equipped with strong springs that hold it closed when the van is moving. This is an important area to check. Make sure the door on the unit you finally buy has some method of keeping the door closed when the van is in motion. If it is inadequately designed in this area, you may end up with a dozen eggs all over your floor.

Examine the hinges on the door carefully. Naturally they should be as free as possible. If they are loose, the hinges have not been adequately installed. This is an area that should be closely examined since it will bear the greatest strain.

199

Consider ease of cleaning when selecting a unit. Since the icebox will be used to store food, it will occasionally need cleaning. This can be simple or it can be a source of frustration. If the unit has been designed with the consumer in mind, cleaning should be easy. Unfortunately the consumer is seldom considered during the design phase. For this reason it is important that you ascertain just how difficult any given unit will be to clean. Units with detachable shelves are easier to clean than ones with fixed shelves. Units that have rounded corners like the one in Fig. 8-19 are much easier to clean since the sponge can more easily reach this area. If the unit is square in the corners like most home appliances are, cleaning will be more difficult. To make them even easier to clean, some have removable doors. This way the door can be removed completely from the van and hosed off.

The final factor to consider when selecting an icebox is the installation. Size, weight, and door opening clearance must be considered before a unit can be installed. For instance, you might buy a unit that has a door that opens from the left; then later discover you need a unit with a door that opens from the right. If you know beforehand what you need, the selection step will be much easier. Some units are designed with reversible doors. That is, the door can be made to open from the right or the left.

Measure the area where you plan on installing an icebox. Be sure to select a spot where the door will have plenty of room to open. Don't install it so close to a table or couch that when the door is open it meets an obstruction.

Refrigerators

Refrigerators for vehicles are more complicated than iceboxes and are, of course, much more expensive. But they are also more functional so the added cost brings added benefits.

There are two types of refrigerators on the market today designed for use in vehicles. One employs a compressor that draws power from the 12-volt battery in the vehicle. It can also be used with 110 volts via a converter. The other type burns propane gas. The latter type is harder to install and more dangerous. But, since it is not connected to the vehicle's battery, there is never any need to worry about the engine not starting.

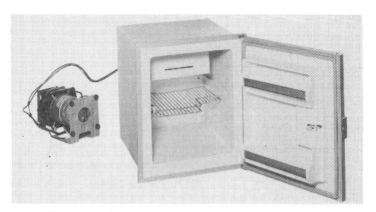

Fig. 8-20. The refrigerator looks much like the icebox. But with a refrigerator, a compressor is needed. This unit uses the 12-volt battery in the vehicle as a source of power.

I would go with the 12-volt system and dual battery arrangement. With the 12-volt unit, all that must be installed is a compressor. No fuel tanks or lines to fool with. The compressor is connected to 12 volts and the refrigerator is immediately operational. Since the refrigerator will draw quite a bit of power from the battery, it should be only used in conjunction with a dual battery system.

If you have decided on the gas type refrigerator, fuel tanks must also be purchased and their selection is an entire new area that must be considered. Also fuel lines must be run from the tank to the unit itself. More decisions to be made. The best way to select a refrigerator of this type is to visit several suppliers and absorb information on their products. Then make a decision based on that knowledge. Of course the basic construction should be carefully examined regardless of what unit you finally select.

A refrigerator that uses 12 volts is relatively simple as shown in Figure 8-20. A compressor and an insulated box are all the parts involved. The compressor is installed as close as practical to the box and is connected to it by wires and the refrigerant line. The distance from the compressor to the box should be kept as short as possible, since increased tubing length results in a loss of cooling.

When installing a refrigerator in your van the manufacturer's recommendations should be followed as closely as possible. But you can observe a few commonsense rules and further increase the efficiency of the installation.

For instance, avoid installing the refrigerator near any source of heat such as the dogbox, auxiliary heater, tec. This simply works the compressor since it must work harder to keep the food cold. Mount the refrigerator as close to the front of the van as is feasible. This way the food inside will be subjected to a far less bumpy ride.

Stoves and Ovens

A stove or oven is probably the most expensive appliance you could include in a van. It is also the most dangerous. Since flame is involved there it is always the fire-hazard factor that must be considered.

Most stoves and ovens run on propane so there are holding tanks and connecting lines involved in addition to the basic unit. One quality manufacturer is Brown Stove Works, Inc. in Cleveland, Tennessee. They market not only the basic counter top burners but complete ranges. They are no less sophisticated than a stove you might see in someone's kitchen. The grates lock in place for travel; the door locks shut. The oven is equipped with a thermostat. In short, all the features you'd expect to see on a range designed for home use are present on some Brown units plus a few extras.

Including a stove in your van is a major undertaking and I suggest you do a lot of soul-searching before undertaking it. The project will be very expensive, time-consuming, and hard to do right. But investing the money and time could net you a really fine van conversion. Also, the value of the van is increased dramatically when a stove is installed. Your van will no longer be just a camper; it will simply be an extension of your own house. So if your goal is owning a rolling penthouse, a stove is something that would really fit your design. Being able to serve hot food while on the move is strong incentive for anyone to include an elaborate appliance like this, but don't let it get the best of you. It is a decision that should not be made lightly.

On to the installation of windows and sunroofs.

Chapter 9

Windows and Sunroofs

WINDOWS

Custom windows are the latest rage. These windows are both attractive and extremely simple to install. The only drawback is a high price. Expect to pay no less than $40 for even a small window for your van.

The selection of custom windows for your van should be easy since many styles are available (Fig. 9-1). Shark's teeth, progressive portholes, and even a Playboy emblem are available. So if your want windows in your van, chances are you'll be able to find something you like.

One of the largest manufacturers of van custom windows is Stretch Forming Corporation located in Fountain Valley, California. Their selection shown in Fig. 9-1, offers a wide variety of styles. Construction of such windows varies little from manufacturer to manufacturer, so comparison shopping for quality won't be as necessary as it is when buying something like cabinets; but you shouldn't take quality for granted. Occasionally a factory second will slip through, so watch for them. The Plexiglas window should be free of scratches and imperfections. The window frame should be inspected carefully. It's made of light aluminum that can bend easily. Many times, damage results from careless handling even before you take delivery. Although manufacturers take special care to package their goods securely, problems do sometimes occur in shipping. Once again, you might be able to save some money by shopping around; for, although quality is usually high, prices can vary widely.

When deciding how many and what styles of windows to install in your van, bear this in mind: It is very easy to overdo

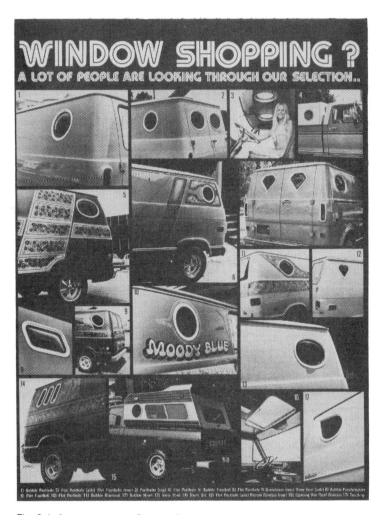

Fig. 9-1. As you can see, Stretch Forming's selection of van windows is, to say the least, vast. Anything from a simple porthole to a Playboy emblem is available. (Courtesy of Stretch Forming Corp.)

WINDOW DESIGNS AND DIMENSIONS

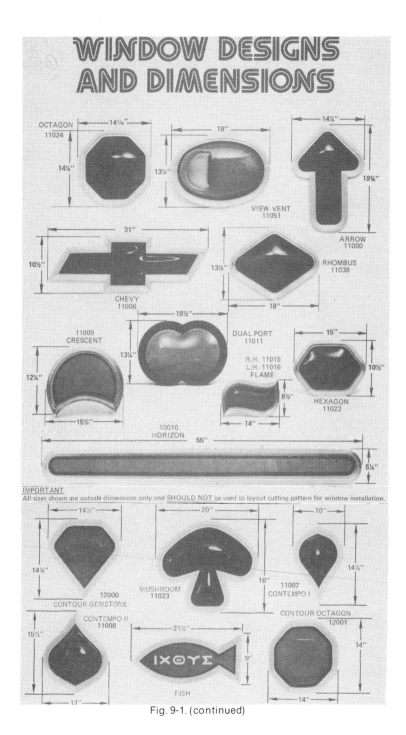

OCTAGON 11024 — 14¼" × 14¼"

VIEW VENT 11051 — 19" × 13⅛"

ARROW 11000 — 14⅛" × 19¾"

CHEVY 11006 — 31" × 10½"

RHOMBUS 11038 — 18" × 13⅛"

11009 CRESCENT — 15½" × 12¾"

DUAL PORT 11011 — 19½" × 13¼"

R.H. 11015 L.H. 11016 FLAME — 14" × 8½"

HEXAGON 11022 — 15" × 10½"

10010 HORIZON — 55" × 5¼"

IMPORTANT
All sizes shown are outside dimensions only and SHOULD NOT be used to layout cutting pattern for window installation.

12000 CONTOUR GEMSTONE — 14½" × 14⅝"

MUSHROOM 11023 — 20" × 16"

11007 CONTEMPO I — 10" × 14½"

CONTEMPO II 11008 — 15½" × 13"

FISH — 21½" × 9"

CONTOUR OCTAGON 12001 — 14" × 14"

Fig. 9-1. (continued)

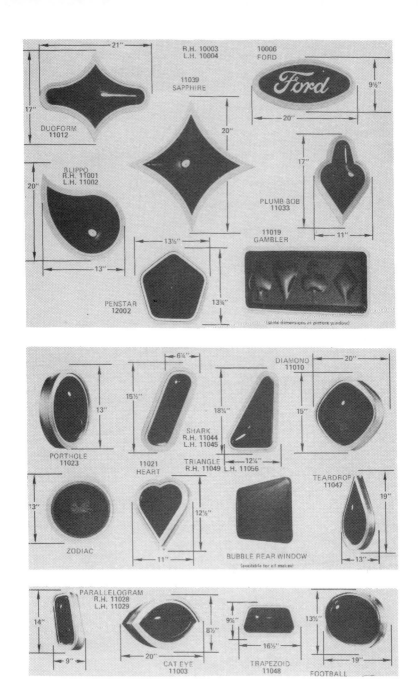

Fig. 9-1. (continued)

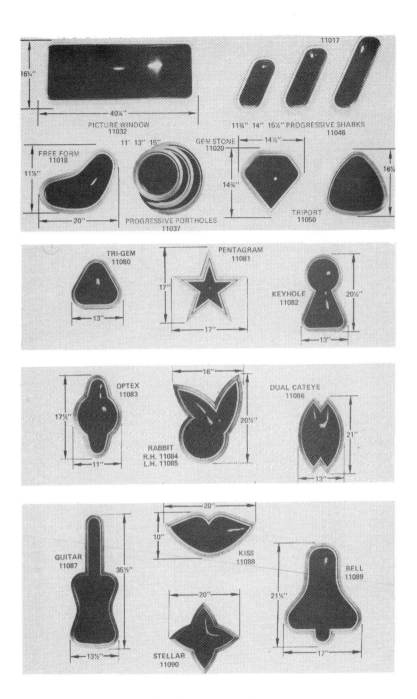

Fig. 9-1. (continued)

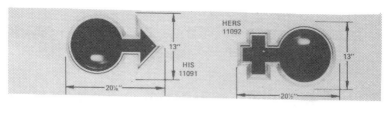

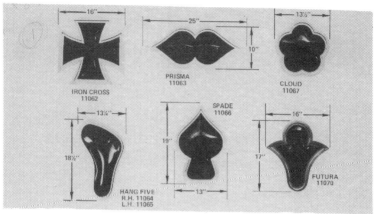

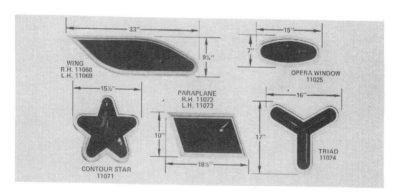

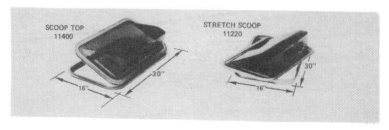

Fig. 9-1. (continued)

Fig. 9-2a. The actual window is installed from the outside while a designer ring is screwed into place from inside the van.

the custom window bit. Very often I see vans rolling down the highway with, in my opinion, too many windows. Instead of adding to the looks of the van, they create a cluttered look. So keep the number of windows down and their design simple.

Incidentally, custom windows are not particularly easy to look through. In fact, they fall far short of the ideal. These windows are used mainly for decoration. If you select an open design as opposed to a small shark's tooth or other tight design, the window will be useful for outside viewing. One reason that custom windows seldom look good in a van is

Fig. 9-2b. All shapes of windows designed for vans are installed the same way. They consist of two components—a designer ring and the window itself.

because people quite often forget the purpose of a window. They get too involved with the esthetics. Everyone wants a custom window because it represents the "converted van." Don't make the same mistake. Remember the purpose of a window is to view the outside world. Select a window that is functional.

Installation

The installation of a van window is surprisingly simple. As Fig. 9-2 shows, there are two pieces to all windows to be mounted in the wall of a van. One piece is the actual window. The second piece is a designer ring that fits over the cut in the wall from the inside of the van. Your first installation step is to make a template (Fig. 9-3). A thin cardboard is the best material to use here. Or simply hold the window in place on the outside of the wall, exactly where you want it mounted, and draw a line around it. Don't make the line circumscribe the outer lip of the window frame. If you do the hole will be too big. The line should be drawn only around the part that will actually go through the wall.

Once the cutting mark has been made on the outside of the van, your next step is to cut out the van wall; use a sabre saw with a metal cutting blade. First, drill a hole somewhere

Fig. 9-3. The first step, once the template has been made, is to trace the outline of the window on the side of the van. Make certain the template does not shift position during this step. Double check your marks to be sure they are correct.

210

Fig. 9-4. A hole is then drilled within the mark to allow the blade of the saw to pass through the metal wall of the van and begin the cut.

within the metal wall area that will be cut away as shown in Fig. 9-4. Use the hole to get the blade into the wall so the area can be cut out.

Cut along the line made denoting the perimeter of the part of the window that will go through the wall. Go slowly and cut carefully. A tolerance of 1/2 inch is necessary. If you deviate more than that, the cut will show after the window is installed. When the metal part has been cut away, remove any insulation that is visible. The blade of the saw should have cut the insulation so it should not be difficult to see what needs to be removed. The next cut is made from the inside of the van. This will be more difficult than cutting the outer wall, so be very careful not to make a mistake.

Drill several holes from the outside of the van through the interior wall. The holes should be positioned along the perimeter of the hole cut in the outer wall. Next, take the template you used for the outer hole and position it on the inside wall lining it up with the positioning hole just drilled. Trace around the template carefully. Insert the saw blade from the inside of the van through one of the holes drilled for positioning the template. Cut along the line traced on the inside wall. While doing this step you can have a friend watch the cutting from the outside to make certain that your cuts are directed properly.

211

When a hole has been cut through both the outer and inner wall of the van and the insulation has been removed, the hardest part is over. Continue by positioning the window from the outside of the van; hold it in place while someone installs the designer ring from inside the van. Screws should be supplied with the window, but if there are not, you can use standard sheet metal screws of suitable length. Once the designer ring is installed, the installation is complete. As the screws that hold the designer ring against the window are tightened, the two pieces will pull together and make a tight seal. Do not overtorque the screws because they strip easily. Tighten them until both pieces have been pulled close enough together to contact the respective walls of the van.

SUNROOFS

The same rules for inspecting windows apply to sunroofs. The Plexiglas and frame are the two main areas to check. If the sunroof is the type that opens, inspect the crank and hinges. They should both work smoothly and be heavy enough to stand the strain of hard use.

A sunroof is going to cost you more than a basic window. You may be surprised just how expensive they are. The high price of windows and sunroofs is probably due to their relative recent introduction to the market and widespread popularity. But then, a ball point pen cost around $20 when first introduced in the late '40s. You'll find these windows a much better bargain.

Installation

The installation of a sunroof is surprisingly similar to that of the window. There are two pieces—a frame containing the actual window and a designer ring that fits over the cut you make in the ceiling from the outside of the van. The hole for the mounting is marked in the same fashion as it was for the window. The only variation is the position. A window could be installed slightly crooked and no one would ever notice (Fig. 9-5). But it is important to cut the mounting hole for a sunroof as square as possible to the van. Measure the distance from the front of the van to both sides of the sunroof and use this measurement to make a square installation. The sunroof should also be centered from side to side.

Fig. 9-5. With the window in place and the designer ring installed, the finished product should look something like this from inside the van. If your walls are covered with shag carpet, be sure to pull the loops from under the designer ring before tightening the screws on the window. This way the extreme edge of the designer ring will be hidden by the carpet.

Cutting the hole through the ceiling will be more difficult because the saw must be held steadier. First, drill a hole from the top of the van for the blade of the saw. Then, with a sabre saw or keyhole saw, cut away the metal part of the ceiling from the top of the van. The blade of the saw should be long enough to cut through both the metal part of the ceiling and the paneling you covered the ceiling with, but if it isn't, a keyhole saw is the ideal tool to finish the cut.

Position the sunroof from the top of the van, put the designer ring in place from the inside of the van, install the screws, and that's almost all there is to it. To prevent either a sunroof or a window from leaking, seal the perimeter with a silicone sealant. This of course, should be done from the outside.

There are only a few odds and ends that must be taken care of before your van is complete. You are almost to Emerald City.

Chapter 10

Finishing Up

Major work on your van is near completion now that you've come this far. In fact, you will, by this time, have received quite a few compliments for your work. Your van is taking on the look of an expensive recreational vehicle. But there are still a few areas to be dealt with before your van can be called finished.

If you haven't already installed molding where needed, this is the time to do so. Special molding is available for around doors and has already been discussed. But an area along the top of either wall remains to be covered. This is probably an unsightly seam in your van where the wall meets the ceiling. But with about an hour's work and a few dollars, you can rectify the situation.

First, visit a local lumber yard. Select a molding style that suits your personal taste and your interior design. If you find nothing appealing, you might even consider designing your own molding. An interesting solution is to use a very large rope, the kind that might be used as hawsers in a shipyard. The rope is secured in place with long screws fixed to the metal wall of the van. Finding rope of a suitable diameter may be difficult and when you do find it you'll be surprised at how expensive it is. But it is an attractive way of handling the problem of hiding the seam along the top of the wall.

Another way to deal with the problem is to use aluminum stripping in place of standard wood molding. It's available at

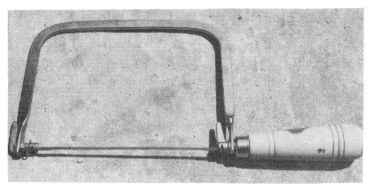

Fig. 10-1. The fine teeth of a coping saw are ideally suited to cutting molding. Since the coping saw is a hand tool, the speed at which the cut is made can be varied, giving the user the control necessary to assure the perfection of the cut.

most hardware stores and looks very nice. It's held in place the same way the rope would be with the exception that shorter screws are used. The aluminum molding gives a more modern look that wouldn't, therefore, be suitable for rustic interior design, but it would be fine for a contemporary motif van.

If you've decided to go with wood molding, you've chosen just about the least expensive. And, the installation is really simple. First, cut the molding to the proper length with a coping saw. Don't try to cut molding with a sabre or Skilsaw; you'll probably be unhappy with the results. These saws don't make the nice clean cuts needed to make molding look good. But a coping saw can cut through molding quickly and cleanly (Fig. 10-1). Measure the length of one of the sides of the van along the top of the wall and cut a piece of molding to that length. Using finishing screws (Fig. 10-2), fasten the molding to the wall as close to the ceiling as possible. If it turns out that the screws must be anchored in the metal wall of the van, you'll need a drill with a bit that is slightly smaller in diameter than the screws used. Drill a hole carefully and install a screw. Screws should be installed approximately six inches apart for best results. Overtorquing the screws will make molding warp.

WINDOW COVERINGS

Until this point window covering has been neglected. Of the several ways to deal with it, one is obvious—curtains. They come in an endless variety from solid colors to four seasons to

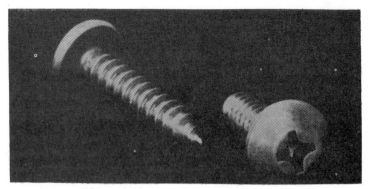

Fig. 10-2. Using decorator screws like these can add a professional touch to your conversion that just isn't possible with standard sheet metal screws. (Courtesy T & H Works Unlimited.)

psychedelic, so there is bound to be something that suits your theme.

Curtains

The best installation is the type that fastens at the bottom as well as the top. Speaking from experience, it is a real irritant to have curtains on the windows that are simply hung from the top (Fig. 10-3). When the windows are down and the van is in motion, curtains flap violently in the wind and frequently block the view of the outside world, making it not

Fig. 10-3. Curtains that are connected at the top only are free to flap in the breeze, causing an obstruction of vision and bothersome noise.

Fig. 10-4. Curtains fastened at the bottom as well as the top can be pulled aside to permit viewing but will not flap around in the wind.

only inconvenient but dangerous from a road safety standpoint. If you are going to include curtains in your van, install them so they are held in place whether the van is moving or not. This type of installation is shown in Fig. 10-4. The curtain can be pulled aside for viewing, or it can be closed for privacy. But the important thing to remember to do is secure your curtains at both the top and bottom.

Installing regular house-type curtain rods is not practical. A different approach must be used. The best solution I've seen

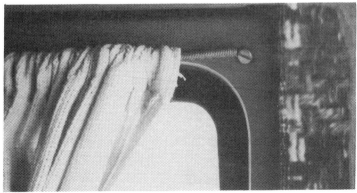

Fig. 10-5. Two screws and a long spring are all that are needed to fashion a very adequate "curtain rod." The spring also serves to absorb shock if the curtain is caught on something or yanked.

so far is the use of long springs (Fig. 10-5). One end of the spring is connected to one side of the window; the other is stretched to the opposite side. Of course, the curtain must be installed on the spring before the spring is mounted. The spring serves as a shock absorber if the curtain ever gets caught on something. Also, the spring is much easier to install than a curtain rod which is not strong enough for this type of installation anyway. A spring through the top of the curtain and one through the bottom will make an ideal window-covering. The type of spring needed for this installation might be a little hard to find. I've seen it in several hardware stores sold as replacement springs for screen doors, but a building supply store might be more likely to stock it.

Shutters

If you've used a rustic or other theme based on wood, covering your windows with shutters would be a great complement to the rear of your van. It will cost more than curtains, but, other than esthetics, there are few advantages to such an installation. The best shutter to use for windows is one that looks like two very small French doors with moveable louvers (Fig. 10-6). When the van is in motion, the louvers can

Fig. 10-6. Installing shutters to cover the windows in your van will require a little special attention, but the added advantage of greater privacy makes that design worthwhile. This shutter is available at department stores as well as building supply stores.

A

B

Fig. 10-7. Covering your windows with reflective material is by far the easiest way to handle the privacy problem. But remember: the one-way mirror effect is not 100%. Under the right conditions it is possible to see into a van that uses this material. Using the patterned reflective material serves a dual function—privacy is attained while at the same time the outside of the van is decorated. (Courtesy of T & H Works, Unlimited.)

be positioned to give the driver adequate visibility. But when privacy is needed, the louvers can be positioned to block out all eyes. And that's the big advantage shutters have over curtains. They afford much more privacy. With a curtain, people can look in your van even with the curtain drawn. But a shutter will effectively hide the interior of the van. Also, a shutter blocks light much more effectively than a curtain.

There's a flood of new gimmicks for the vanner. In that flood is included reflective material for windows. Available in patterns or just shiny (Fig. 10-7A and B), in effect, it turns a normal window into a 2-way mirror. From the outside, the window looks like mirrors, but from the inside the window looks "normal" (you can see through them) except for a slight tint. However, 2-way effect is not 100 percent perfect. It is possible, under certain lighting conditions, to see *into* a van equipped with mirror decals. Nevertheless, it greatly lessens the ease with which a stranger can look in. Reflective material also serves another purpose, it reflects the energy of the sun and, thus, keeps the van much cooler (Fig. 10-8). This is a big advantage for vans that will be used where the sun is very bright most of the day. This reflective film is expensive, but when you consider what it does for you and your van, it makes it worth it.

So much for covering the windows. Between curtains, shutters, and reflective film you should be able to come up

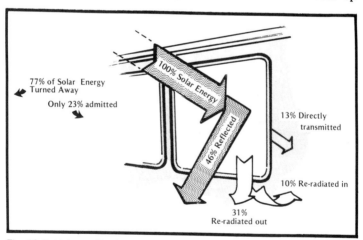

Fig. 10-8. Using reflective sheeting to cover your windows can also aid in keeping your van cool by reflecting a large percentage of the sun's energy. (Courtesy of Van Mail.)

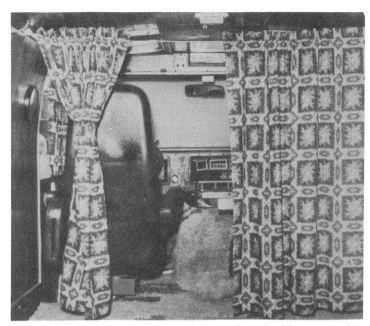

Fig. 10-9. To separate the rear area of the van from the driver area and to increase privacy, curtains are installed just behind the two front seats. They can be pulled aside when added visibility is needed for driving. (Courtesy of T & H Works, Unlimited.)

with a design that pleases you. You can even mix and match. Cover the rear windows with shutters and cover the side windows with reflective film. A curtain can be used to seal off the rear area of the van from the driver area as in Fig. 10-9. Create!

CARPETING

The task of carpeting your van has been deferred to these pages to avoid damage to the carpet during the preceding conversion process. Now that the van is all but done, it is safe to add beautiful carpet to your interior. First, we'll consider the selection.

Carpet is too big an investment to make without careful planning. It can represent as much as 20 percent of your total room furnishings. With the myriad texture/fiber combinations available on today's market, it is no wonder that vanners are confused when they begin to consider this important purchase. To help you choose wisely, here are some clues from Armstrong Carpets to problem-free shopping.

First, make a plan by measuring the total area to be covered. Be sure to make your measurements on the safe side to avoid buying too little. Wearability is what most people look for, and you should consider traffic in this case. Pile density is an important factor in durability. If the pile is thick, packed tightly, and resilient, chances are the carpet will wear well. Check the pile density by bending back a corner of the carpet. The old rule—the deeper, the denser, the better—will always apply.

Construction

Most carpet today is tufted. To put it simply, fiber is pushed through a backing to form little loops called tufts. The yarn that appears on the surface is either left as loops or is cut. There are many variations of cut and uncut pile carpets.

Level-loop, two level-loop are exactly what their names imply. Shag and plush are two variations of cut pile, and there are even combinations of cut-and-loop pile for different visuals as in the hottest new look—sculptured shag. As a general rule shag provides a formal or informal look depending on the height and density of the pile. Plushes are decidedly formal, and their tendency to show footprints like velvet is part of their appeal.

In high-traffic areas, level-loops work best and is why this construction is used almost exclusively in commercial buildings. Level-loop now come in some very colorful prints ideal for vans since the pattern tends to mask fine lint and dust.

Fibers

Versatility and beauty are not the only virtues of today's technological advances. Man-made fibers developed for carpet manufacture in special lengths, thicknesses, and colors have never been easier to care for. All man-made fibers have these qualities in common: They clean well, are mildew-proof, mothproof, and non-allergenic.

Most of the confusion in buying carpet lies in the identification of fiber. While the consumer is subjected to literally hundreds of fiber brand names, there are, in fact, only four basic man-made fiber types used in carpet today: nylon, acrylic, polyester, and polypropylene. Each of these fibers has its own specific properties. For instance, nylon soils more easily than other fibers but makes up for it by being the longest wearing. Acrylic resembles wool more closely than any other man-made fiber, but has none of its disadvantages—one of which is high cost. Polyester is sturdy and luxurious as nylon but less springy. Hard-wearing polypropylene—often labeled Olefin—gained fame as outdoor carpeting, but innovations in construction have made it excellent for indoors as well despite its lack of resilience. And of course, two or more of these four fibers can be used together to take advantage of the outstanding characteristics of each.

Padding

Since padding is a must, get the best you can afford. Padding protects your investment by extending the life of your carpeting. It also adds comfort, absorbs shock, and insulates against noises, heat, and cold. Many fine-quality carpets have a built-in high-density rubber-cushioned backing which not only gives uniform support but cuts down on installation costs.

Color

To the average shopper, color is the most important consideration from a decorating standpoint. Once you've established where the carpet is to be used and have selected the most suitable construction, then the color of the carpeting can be dealt with. One of the biggest fashion trends today is pattern-dyed carpet with a range of textures and colorations you have to see to believe. Where color is concerned, it's well to remember that no matter the texture or pile height, solid colors (pale, medium, or dark) show more dirt than patterns. Widely spaced patterns show less dirt than solids but more than smaller compact patterns. Multi-tweeds show less dirt than any of the others.

INSTALLATION

Carpeting your van is not a job that should be done in haste. If anything is going to demand patience in your conversion, it will be the carpeting step. The carpet has the job of hiding any little mistakes you've made in cutting the floor pieces, lining up the plywood, and the unfinished area long the bottom of the walls. It is a step that must be done slowly. Probably nobody can carpet a van in a couple of hours without making mistakes. Resign yourself to that fact at the outset. A wrong cut in the carpet can end up costing you $100, so be careful.

The Tools

The tools needed to do an effective job of carpeting are very common ones. Here is a basic list:

- Hammer
- Utility knife with extra blades
- Marker
- Scissors
- Staple gun
- Two extra hands

In addition to the basic tools mentioned, you'll need some carpet tacks or contact cement to hold the carpet in place. The tacks work fine for shag carpet but if you are going to install indoor/outdoor carpet contact cement is best. To make your installation look really professional, use molding to hold the edge of the carpet down next to the doors. It comes as aluminum stripping and is available at carpet stores. Be sure to have about six extra blades on hand for the utility knife. Carpet dulls them fast and it is impossible to make nice clean cuts with a dull knife.

With all this junk accumulated (plus about five square yards of really fine carpet and padding) you're ready to begin.

First, remove anything from the van that is not bolted down. Get as many of the obstacles out of your way as you can. If you're really ambitious, remove the two front seats again as you did in the installation of the floor. This will give you quite a bit of extra room and will make it easier to carpet under them.

Installing The Padding

Naturally, padding must be installed first. This is a very simple step. Simply spread the padding out over the floor as evenly as possible and staple it down in a few places to hold it still while you trim away the excess around the edges. This is done with the scissors. The utility knife will cut through the padding, but scissors will do it much more quickly. When trimming the excess padding away, cut only enough off to allow the padding to lie flat. Ideally, the padding should extend to the wall—no more and no less. This step is not critical, but doing it carefully gives you a chance to make mistakes before you tackle the carpet cutting job.

When all excess padding has been trimmed away, staple the padding to the floor so that there are no buckles and no chance of the padding shifting. Clean the scraps out of the van and prepare to install the carpet.

Installing The Carpet

This procedure must be carried out with much more precision than the padding step. It means it will take you considerably longer. Be sure to allow yourself enough time to do a good job. With a friend's help, three hours should be enough to completely carpet the back of your van.

Spread the piece of carpet over the floor as you did with the padding. Tack it down in a few places. Make sure it is tacked securely enough to prevent it moving in this step. If it does, your cuts will not be straight and you could ruin the carpet. With a sharp utility knife, pick a point along the base of the wall and begin trimming away the excess carpet. After you've cut through about four inches of carpet, test-fit the edge and make sure it falls close (but not too close) to the wall. If your cut is a little off, compensate for it by cutting further in or out, whichever is needed. Cut for a few more inches and repeat this process. Do not cut out four feet of carpet and then test fit the piece. If you do and your cut is very far off, you have made an irreparable mistake. Every four inches or so, check to see that your cut is on target. After you've cut about five feet of carpet, you'll begin to get the feel of it and it'll go easier. Remember, it's very easy to get overconfident when cutting carpet—that's the first step to making mistakes.

If it's necessary to trim carpet around wheel wells, you'll want to proceed more slowly than you would on a straight-away. Check to see that your cut is on target about every two inches. When you're out of the trouble area, go back to checking every four inches.

If, after you've trimmed all the excess carpet away, you can see that your cuts are not as straight as you would like, there is a way to hide them. Simply install molding along the entire perimeter of the floor. This will hide the actual cut and add a very professional look to your installation. Also it will help hold the carpet in place. Aluminum molding is only one type that will work in this application. Just about any type of regular wood or plastic molding that suits your interior design will be fine.

When all the extra carpet has been trimmed away, your van should look finished. In fact, you probably want to sit back and enjoy your handywork. But don't! The carpet must be tacked down in enough places to keep it from shifting during use. Also, tacking it down will eliminate buckles caused by the carpet not being held tightly against the floor. If you've used shag, carpet tacks will do fine to hold it in place. Use your finger to clear a place in the pile for the tack. Spread the pile apart so the carpet backing is exposed. If the carpet is really thick this is not going to be easy. But it should be done. Once you've found the carpet backing, tack it down. The reason for all this separating is simply to keep any of the strands from being trapped under the head of the tack and leaving an unsightly tack identification pit! If the pile is spread apart before the tack is installed, no such indentation is left.

It's quite likely that the piece of carpet you bought will not cover the entire floor in one piece. It may be cut and sewn together in a slightly different shape. If this is necessary in your van, invest in some high-quality carpet thread and a good curved needle. These two items will make the task of piecing carpet together much easier.

After the two cut pieces are installed they must be sewn together to form a neat seam. Stitches should be about three-eighths of an inch in from the edge of the carpet for adequate strength. If they are only 1/4-inch from the edge, they can tear out—a real pain to fix. Pull the thread tight after each stitch. If you make three stitches and then try to pull the thread tight you're going to discover that you can't do it. But if they are pulled tight after each stitch, there should be no problem.

Tack the carpet adequately to the floor. If you've selected indoor/outdoor carpet, contact cement can be used to hold the carpet in place. Since the glue will be holding the carpet to the padding, it is necessary to tack the edges of the carpet down with tacks. The contact cement will work fine for the open spaces in the middle of the floor, but it will not work well for holding the edge down.

For all practical purposes, your conversion job is complete. The carpet is down, the walls are finished, the ceiling is covered. So the overall effect is one of completion. Now you can really start to enjoy your van. But to make it even more enjoyable, you might consider adding a few accessories.

Accessories

The fixed-up van market is highly lucrative and the manufacturers know it. So the market has been saturated with

Fig. 10-10. A nice addition to any van would be a digital clock like one of these marketed by T & H Works, Unlimited. Features include automatic brightness control for the display, wrong time indicator, and 24 hour alarm.

all kinds of little goodies to catch the consumer's eye. For instance, Fig. 10-10 shows three different styles of quartz digital readout clocks marketed by T & H Works Unlimited. One style is for in-dash mounting, the other two are designed to be mounted on or over the dash. The clocks are pretty expensive, but they boast lots of features like a 24-hour alarm, automatic brightness control for the display, and a wrong time (due to interrupted power) indicator. So if you want to add a

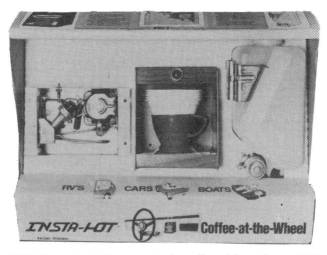

Fig. 10-11. If you don't like stopping for coffee while on the road, this hot water dispenser manufactured by Federal Water Dynamics in Palos Verdes, California may be for you. The hot water can be used for lots of other things like soup, cocoa, tea. (Courtesy of T & H Works, Unlimited.)

classy gadget, a digital clock is a nice way to go. Then, you can sleep in your van and not worry about being late. Just set the alarm and forget it.

For heavy coffee drinkers the same outfit markets a hot water dispenser manufactured by Federal Water Dynamics (Fig. 10-11). It can be used for soup, tea, or anything that just needs hot water. The unit does not do actual mixing of the brew; it only dispenses hot water. But even at that it would be a great addition for those long trips across country when a cup of coffee is all you need.

For the top of the engine cover there are countless varieties of drink trays. (Fig. 10-12). Just supply them with the make and year of your van and they'll supply you with a drink tray that is designed to fit that van. Some of the trays have storage compartments included. All are covered with Formica to make them almost impervious to moisture and heat.

For the floor of your van up front, and to help protect your carpet, there are coco mats. Again, all you need to do is give the manufacturer the make and year of your van and they can supply you with coco mats designed to fit. The coco mats shown in Fig. 10-13 are a fair representation of the mats available from many manufacturers so don't buy the first ones you see. Shop around. As I've said, the van market is highly

Fig. 10-12. For the top of the engine cover snack trays are available. The units are designed for specific vans so the year and make of yours is essential when ordering. (Courtesy of T & H Works.)

competitive and you can usually get a better deal if you compare prices of different manufacturers.

For a really expensive modification, around $350, you can replace factory seats with reclining buckets as shown in Fig. 10-14. Similar seats are available through Ford, Dodge, and the

Fig. 10-13. For the floor in the front of your van, coco mats are marketed that are designed to fit specific years and makes. Coco mats resist moisture, are extremely long-wearing, and relatively inexpensive. (Courtesy of T & H Works, Unlimited.)

Fig. 10-14. If you're interested in replacing those stock seats in your van, reclining buckets like this one are the way to go. The armrests fold up out of the way and the whole seat swivels as well. (Courtesy of T & H Works, Unlimited.)

other big names in vehicles, but they are usually quite a bit more expensive than those available on the open market. And again, different colors, styles, and prints are available to suit just about every van decor.

The list of accessories could go on and on. The market has been literally flooded with manufacturers' products; everybody is trying to capitalize on the recent popularity of the converted van. This makes for lots of competition. Many of the accessories are useful; but many more aren't. Watch what you buy. Don't be swayed by sensational advertising. Buy what you can use, not what you are told you can use.

Enjoy your van. It should be a source of pride for years to come. You have just accomplished what many people would love to do. You now own a valuable vehicle. The converson job should add at least $1500 to the value of your van. Consider it when you decide to sell. You have reached the Emerald City.

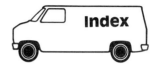

Index

A

Accsssories   226
Appliances   49
   heaters   206
   iceboxes   208
   ovens   202
   refrigerators   200
   selection   160, 196
   stoves   202
Automatic
   reversing, tape transport   72
   shutoff, tape transport   73

B

Balance controls, for sound system
     69, 72
Bar   45
Bed
   construction   174
   proper placement   35
   types available   36

C

Carpet
   installation   225
   padding, installation   224
Carpeting   221
   color   223
   construction   222
   fibers   222
   installation   223
   padding   223
Cartridge, tape deck   64
Cassette tape deck   64
Ceiling
   considerations   142
   covering   156
   covering material   148
   installation   149
   installation, tools   149
   installing a sunroof   145
   insulation   148
   lighting fixtures   158
   lights   142
   lights, placement   144
   paneling   136
Checklist after van is test driven   27

Commercial service, as
     van market   20
Constructed furniture   169
Construction
   of a shelf   189
   of bed   174
   of bed crosswise   181
   of bed lengthwise   174
   of table   169
Corners, paneling   125

D

Doors
   covering   110, 139
   paneling   127
   relation to van selection   15
Doorway, paneling   136

E

Engine placement, in relation
     to van selection   10

F

Fiberglass, insulation   114
Finalizing deal on the van   29
Finishing touches   214
Floor installation   53
   insulation   53
   plywood   54
   tools   54
Foam insulation   114
Forward-mounted engine
   advantages   15
   disadvantages   13
Frequency response, tape decks   76
Furniture
   constructed   169
   selection   160

G

Government, as van market   20
Ground clearance, relation
     to van selection   18

H

Heaters, types   196
Height, in relation to size   9

I

Iceboxes, selection criteria   198
In-cab engine   12
   disadvantages   11
Interior
   appointments   50
   planning   30
Installation
   carpet padding   224
   carpeting   223
   ceiling   149
   lighting fixtures   158
   paneling   121
   power system   103
   wall insulation   120
   walls, installation   120
   wiring   103
Installing the carpet   225
Insulating the ceiling   148
Insulation
   first step in floor installation   53
   for walls   114
   laying for floor   59
Inverters   92

L

Lever-action latching mechanism   15
Lighting   48
   choices   93
   fixtures, ceiling   158
   fusing   97
   placement   94
   switching   96
Lights
   ceiling   142
   selection   98

M

Matrix, quad   68
Mirrors
   installation   140

measuring for wall covering 116
Mounting
  holes for ceiling 151
  holes for paneling 122
  tape decks 75

N

Newspaper. for van market 21

O

Options. in van selection 19
Ovens 202

P

Panel covering. installation 138
Paneling
  a doorway 136
  allowing for mounting holes 122
  around wheel wells 125
  as wall installation 103
  corners 125
  doors 127
  installation 121
  measuring for 115
  mounting around
  problem areas 124
  quantity 118
  rear doors 128
  sliding doors 132
  the ceiling 136
Partitions 32
  construction 133
  covering 112
  use of 110
Planning van interior 30
Plywood
  covering on walls 108
  fitting for floor 56
  for floor installation 54
  laying for floor 62
Power
  output of tape decks 80
  system 90
  system. installation 103
  two-battery 90
Prefabricated furniture.
  examination 193
Purchased furniture 190
Purchasing checklist 23

Q

Quad
  matrix 68
  sound system 46

R

Refrigerators
  installation 201
  selection 200

S

Seating 39
  bench 40
  factory-built 40
  swivel-type bucket 42
Selection of proper van 7
Sensitivity of tape decks 80
Shelf construction 189
Size
  height 9
  in relation to van selection 7
  wheelbase 8
  width 8
Slammable type latching
  mechanism 15
Sliding doors 16
Speakers
  amount of power 82
  selection 81
Specifications of tape decks 76
Sound system 46. 64
  balance controls 69
  tape transport 70
  tone controls 68
  volume controls 70
  wiring 85
Stereo sound system 46
Storage units 44
Stoves 202
Sunroofs
  installation 212
  placement 147
  types 145
Switches. selection 99

T

Table 37
  building 169
Tape
  decks. mounting 75
  transport. automatic reversing 72

transport. automatic shutoff 73
  transport. sound system 70
Test drive of your vehicle 25
Tone controls. for sound system 68
Tools
  for ceiling installation 149
  for installation of walls 120
  for installing carpeting 224
  needed for floor installation 54
Two-battery power system 90
Types of sunroof 145

U

Upholstery material as
  wall covering 116
Upholstery material. over paneling
   138
used car lot. as van market 21

V

Van
  accessories 226
  selection. where to
  find the market 19
Volume controls. sound system 70

W

Wall
  covering. judging amount 16
  covering material. quantity 119
  covering with plywood 108
  insulation 114
  paneling 103
  proper measuring
  for paneling 121
  variations 103
Wheel wells. paneling 124
Wheelbase. in relation to size 8
Width-in relation to size 8
Window
  coverings 215
  coverings. curtains 216
  coverings. shutters 218
  installation 210
  relation to van selection 17
  selection 203
Wire. selection 101
Wiring
  final planning 102
  for sound system 85
  fusing 97
  installation 103